The Institute of Paper Chemistry

Appleton, Wisconsin

Bibliographic Series

NUMBER 185
SUPPLEMENT II

Flameproofing

JACK WEINER AND LILLIAN ROTH

1972

ABBREVIATIONS USED IN THE INSTITUTE BIBLIOGRAPHIC SERIES

A.	Angstrom unit(s), 10^{-10} m.
AB.	Aktiebolag(et)
ABIPC	Abstract Bulletin of The Institute of Paper Chemistry
abs.	absolute
abstr.	abstract(s)
abstrd.	abstracted
Ac	acetyl, CH_3CO- [in chemical formulas only]
a.c.	alternating current
acad.	academic, academy
ACS	American Chemical Society
a.d.	airdry
addn.	addition
addnl.	additional
admin.	administration, administrative
AFNOR	Association Francaise de Normalisation
AG.	Aktiengesellschaft
agr.	agricultural, agriculture
AIChE	American Institute of Chemical Engineers
AITIPE	Asociacion de Investigacion Tecnica de la Industria Papelera Espanola
alc.	alcohol, alcoholic
alk.	alkaline [not alkali!]
alky.	alkalinity
Am.	American
amp.	ampere(s)
amt.	amount [noun only]
A.N.	Akademiya Nauk
anal.	analysis, analytical
anald.	analyzed
analg.	analyzing
anat.	anatomical
anhyd.	anhydride, anhydrous
anon.	anonymous
APA	American Pulpwood Assocn.
API	American Paper Institute
app.	apparatus
APPITA	Australian & New Zealand Pulp & Paper Industry Technical Assocn.
Appita	Journal of APPITA
appl.	applied [in journal names]
applg.	applying
appln.	application
approx.	approximate(ly)
aq.	aqueous
AS.	Aktieselskab(et); use for A/S
ASP	activated sludge process
assoc.	associate
assocd.	associated
assocg.	associating
assocn.	association
assocs.	associates [noun only!]
ASTM	American Society for Testing and Materials
ATCP	Asociacion Mexicana de Tecnicos de las Industrias de la Celulosa y del Papel, a.c.
ATIP	Association Technique de l'Industrie Papetiere
atm.	atmosphere(s), atmospheric
ATS	Associated Technical Services, Inc. (East Orange, N.J. 07019)
at.wt.	atomic weight
Aug.	August
Austral.	Australian
autom.	automatic(ally), automation
av.	average [not as a verb!]
bacteriol.	bacteriology, bacteriological(ly)
BHC	benzene hexachloride, hexachlorocyclohexane
bibl.	bibliographic, bibliography
biol.	biological, biology
BIPC	Bulletin of The Institute of Paper Chemistry [changed to ABIPC with Volume 29]
BOD	biochemical oxygen demand
bot.	botanical(ly)
b.p.	boiling point
Brit.	British
Bros.	Brothers [in company names]
Btu	British thermal unit(s)
Bu	butyl [in chemical formulas only]
Bulg.	Bulgaria(n)
Bull.	Bulletin
Bz	benzoyl, C_6H_5CO- [not benzyl!]
C.	degree(s) Centigrade, degree(s) Celsius
c[date]	copyrighted
ca.	circa: about
CA	cellulose acetate
CAB	cellulose acetate-butyrate
cadoxene	cadmium ethylenediamine
cal.	calorie(s)
calc.	calculate
calcd.	calculated
calcg.	calculating
calcn.	calculation
Calif.	California(n)
Can.	Canada, Canadian
CAP	cellulose acetate-propionate
C&B	Cross and Bevan [cellulose]
cc.	cubic centimeter
CDA	cellulose diacetate
CEC	carboxyethylcellulose
CF	Canadian [standard] freeness
cf.	compare, see also
CFSTI	Clearinghouse for Federal Scientific & Technical Information [U.S. Dept. of Commerce] [now NTIS]
charac.	characteristic
characd.	characterized
characg.	characterizing
characn.	characterization
chem.	chemistry [not chemist!]; chemical(ly) [not as noun!]
Chin.	Chinese
chromat.	chromatographic, chromatography
Cia.	Companhia, Compania
Cie.	Compagnie
cm.	centimeter(s)
CMC	carboxymethylcellulose
c.m.d.	cross-machine direction(al)
CMT	Concora Medium Test
CN	cellulose nitrate
Co.	Company
COD	chemical oxygen demand
coeff.	coefficient
Coll.	College
com.	commercial
comm.	committee, commission
commun.	communication
conc.	concentrate
concd.	concentrated
concg.	concentrating
concn.	concentration
conf.	conference
const.	constant
contg.	containing
copolymd.	copolymerized
copolymg.	copolymerizing
copolymn.	copolymerization
Corp.	Corporation
corresp.	corresponding
c.p.	chemically pure
cp.	centipoise(s)
cpd.	compound
cpn.	composition
CPPA	Canadian Pulp & Paper Assocn.
cps	cycles per second, hertz units
crit.	critical(ly)
cryst.	crystalline
crystd.	crystallized
crystg.	crystallizing
crystn.	crystallization
crysty.	crystallinity
CSIRO	Commonwealth Scientific & Industrial Research Organization
CTA	cellulose triacetate
cu.	cubic
cuam	cuprammonium hydroxide
cuene	cupriethylenediamine
cu.m.	cubic meter(s)
CX	cellulose xanthate
Czechosl.	Czechoslovakia(n)
d.	density
Dan.	Danish
DAS	Deutsche Auslegeschrift
dbh	diameter at breast height
d.c.	direct current
DEAE	diethylaminoethyl
Dec.	December
decpn.	decomposition
deg.	degree(s)
dep.	dependent, depending
depolymd.	depolymerized
depolymg.	depolymerizing
depolymn.	depolymerization
dept.	department
deriv.	derivative
det.	determine
detd.	determined
detg.	determining
detn.	determination
devd.	developed
devg.	developing
devt.	development
DHP	dehydrogenation polymer (synthetic lignin)
diam.	diameter
dil.	dilute
dild.	diluted
dilg.	diluting
diln.	dilution
DIN	Deutsche Industrie-Norm [German industrial standard]
discn.	discussion
dissoc.	dissociate
dissocd.	dissociated
dissocg.	dissociating
dissocn.	dissociation
distd.	distilled
distg.	distilling
distn.	distillation
div.	division
dm.	decimeter(s)
DMF	dimethyl formamide
DMS	dimethyl sulfide
DMSO	dimethyl sulfoxide
DOS	Deutsche Offenlegungschrift
DP	degree(s) of polymerization
DS	degree(s) of substitution
DTA	differential thermal analysis
EC	ethylcellulose
ed.	edition, editor(s)
EDTA	ethylenediamine tetraacetic acid
educ.	education, educational
e.g.	exempli gratia: for example
elec.	electric(al,-ally)
elecy.	electricity
elem.	elementary
elt.	element
emf.	electromotive force
encl.	enclosure
ENCC	Ente Nazionale per la Cellulosa e per la Carta
eng.	engineering
Engl.	English
engr.	engineer
entomol.	entomology, entomological
equil.	equilibrium, equilibria
equiv.	equivalent
esp.	especially
ESR	electron (paramagnetic) spin resonance
est.	estimate
estd.	estimated
estg.	estimating
estn.	estimation
Et	ethyl [in chemical formulas only]
etc.	et cetera: and so forth
Ets.	Etablissement(s)
e.v.	electron volt(s)
e.V.	eingetragener Verein [registered organization]
eval.	evaluate
evald.	evaluated
evalg.	evaluating
evaln.	evaluation
evap.	evaporate
evapd.	evaporated
evapg.	evaporating
evapn.	evaporation
evoln.	evolution

EWNN	Eisen-Weinsaure-Natron in Natronlauge [Fe–Na tartrate complex in NaOH]	IR	infrared	natl.	national
exam.	examination	irradg.	irradiating	NCASI	National Council [of the Paper Industry] for Air & Stream Improvement, Inc.
examd.	examined	irradn.	irradiation		
examg.	examining	ISO	International Standardization Organization	NE	Northeast, northeastern
excl.	excluded, excluding, exclusive(ly)	Ital.	Italian	neg.	negative
		IUFRO	International Union of Forest Research Organizations	Neth.	Netherlands
expt.	experiment			neut.	neutral
exptl.	experimental(ly)			neutd.	neutralized
ext.	extract	J.	journal	neutg.	neutralizing
extd.	extracted	Jan.	January	neutn.	neutralization
extg.	extracting	Jap.	Japanese	NII	Nauchno-Issledovatel'skii Institut [Research Institute]
extn.	extraction				
extv.	extractive	K.	degree(s) Kelvin	NLL	National Lending Library for Science & Technology (Boston Spa, York.)
		kc.	kilocycle(s)		
F.	degree(s) Fahrenheit	kcal.	kilocalorie(s)	nm.	nanometer(s), 10^{-9} m. (formerly mμ, millimicron)
Fa.	Firma; Company, Firm	kg.	kilogram(s)		
Feb.	February	KG.	Kommandit-Gesellschaft (auf Aktien)	NMR	nuclear magnetic resonance
FEFCO	Federation Europeenne des Fabriquants du Carton Ondule	kHz	kilohertz	no.	number(s)
		KK.	Kabushiki Kaisha, Co. Ltd.	Norw.	Norwegian
FeTNa	See EWNN	km.	kilometer(s)	Nov.	November
Finn.	Finnish	KMW	Karlstads Mekaniska Werkstadter AB.	n.p.	narodni podnik: state-owned enterprise
fld.	followed				
flg.	following	kp.	kilopond(s); kilogram force in contrast to kilogram mass	NPIRI	National Printing Ink Research Institute (Bethlehem, Pa.)
FOGRA	Deutsche Gesellschaft fur Forschung im Grafischen Gewerbe [German Society for Printing Research, Munich]	kv.	kilovolt(s)	NRC	National Research Council
		kw.	kilowatt(s)	NTC	National Translation Center, John Crerar Library (Chicago, Ill. 60616)
		kw.-hr.	kilowatt-hour(s)		
f.p.	freezing point			NTIS	National Technical Information Service [formerly CFSTI] (Springfield, Va. 22151)
fpm	feet per minute	lab.	laboratory		
fps	feet per second	lb.	pound(s)		
Fr.	French	LC	lignocellulose	NV.	Naamloze Vennootschap
ft.	foot, feet	L.D.	lethal dose	NW	Northwest, northwestern
ft.-lb.	foot-pound(s)	lib.	library		
		lit.	literary, literature	o-	ortho-
γ	gamma-number or gamma-value: D.S. of a polymer in terms of substituent groups per 100 monomer units	ln	natural (base e) logarithm	Oct.	October
		log	decimal logarithm	o.d.	ovendry; bonedry; absolutely dry
		LS	lignosulfonate(s)	OHG.	Offene Handelsgesellschaft
		LSA	lignosulfonic acid(s)	org.	organic
g.	gram(s)	Ltd.	Limited-liability company	ORP	oxidation-reduction potential
GA.	Gemeinschaftsanschluss [in company names]			oxidg.	oxidizing
		μ-	micro- [as unit prefix only!] 10^{-6}	oxidn.	oxidation
gal.	gallon(s)			Oy.	Osakeyhtio
GATF	Graphic Arts Technical Foundation	m.	meter(s) [not instruments]	oz.	ounce(s)
GE	General Electric [brightness units]	m-	meta-		
		M	molar; molecular weight/liter	p.	page(s)
Gebr.	Gebruder; Brothers [in company names]	ma.	milliampere(s)	p-	para-
		mag.	magazine	PAA	polyacrylamide
gen.	general(ly)	math.	mathematical, mathematics	PAN	polyacrylonitrile
geogr.	geographic(ally)	matl.	material	pat.	patent
geom.	geometric(ally)	max.	maximum	patd.	patented
Ger.	German	Mc.	megacycle(s)	PBAN	polybutadiene-acrylonitrile
GFL	Grafiska Forsknings-Laboratoriet [Graphic Research Lab., Stockholm]	MC	methylcellulose	pbd.	paperboard
		M.C.	machine-coated	PBS	polybutadiene-styrene
		m.d.	machine direction(al)	PE	polyethylene
GLC	gas-liquid chromatography	Me	methyl, CH_3 [in chemical formulas only]	PEG	polyethylene glycol
GmbH.	Gesellschaft mit beschrankter Haftung			PEI	polyethylene imine
		mech.	mechanical	PEO	poly(ethylene oxide)
govt.	government	MEK	methyl ethyl ketone	PET	poly(ethylene terephthalate)
GPO	Government Printing Office	meq.	milliequivalent	PF	phenol-formaldehyde
		Mev	million electron volt	pH	hydrogen-ion concentration
ha.	hectare(s); 2.471 acres	MF	melamine-formaldehyde	Ph	phenyl, C_6H_5- [not phenol!] (in chemical formulas only)
HEC	hydroxyethylcellulose	M.F.	machine finish, mill finish		
hf	high frequency	mfd.	manufactured	phot.	photographic, photography
horiz.	horizontal(ly)	mfg.	manufacturing	phys.	physical, physics
hp	horse power(s)	mfr.	manufacture(r)	physiol.	physiological, physiology
HPC	hydroxypropylcellulose	μg.	microgram(s), 10^{-6} g.	PIMA	Paper Industry Management Assocn.
hr.	hour(s)	mg.	milligram(s)	PIRA	Research Association for the Paper and Board, Printing and Packaging Industries
Hung.	Hungarian	MG	machine-glazed		
Hz	hertz	min.	minute(s); minimum		
		misc.	miscellaneous, miscellany	pkd.	packaged
i.e.,	id est: that is	mixt.	mixture	pkg.	packaging
IGT	Instituut voor Graafische Techniek (Amsterdam); Institut fur Grafische Technik (Leipzig)	M.L.D.	minimum lethal dose	p.l.i.	pounds per linear inch
		ml.	milliliter(s)	PMA	polymethyl acrylate
		μm.	micrometer(s), 10^{-6} m. [not instruments!] (formerly written μ, micron)	pmkg.	papermaking
illus.	illustrated, illustrating, illustration			PMMA	polymethyl methacrylate
		mm.	millimeter(s)	PMR	proton magnetic resonance
Inc.	Incorporated	mol.	molecule, molecular	PMRL	Pulp Manufacturers Research League (formerly Sulfite Pulp Manufacturers Research League)
incl.	including, inclusive(ly)	mol.wt.	molecular weight		
ind.	industrial, industry	morphol.	morphology, morphological	Pol.	Polish
indep.	independent(ly)	m.p.	melting point	polymd.	polymerized
inorg.	inorganic	mp	millipoise, 10^{-3} poise	polymg.	polymerizing
insol.	insoluble	MS	moles of substituent combined	polymn.	polymerization
Inst.	Institute	MUF	melamine-urea-formaldehyde	Port.	Portuguese
instr.	instrument	mv.	millivolt(s)	pos.	positive
instrl.	instrumental	MWD	mol.wt. distribution	PP	polypropylene
instrn.	instrumentation	MWL	milled wood lignin	ppm	parts per million
intern.	international			PPRIC	Pulp & Paper Research Institute of Canada
IPC	Institute of Paper Chemistry	N	normal; equivalent weight/liter		
IPREIG	Institut Professionnel de Recherche et d'Etudes des Industries Graphiques	NAS	National Academy of Science(s)	ppt.	precipitate
		NASA	National Aeronautics and Space Administration	pptd.	precipitated
				pptg.	precipitating

pptn.	precipitation
Pr	propyl, C_3H_7- [in chemical formulas only]
pract.	practical(ly)
prelim.	preliminary
prep.	prepare
prepd.	prepared
prepg.	preparing
prepn.	preparation
prod.	product
prodg.	producing
prodn.	production
prop.	property
PS	polystyrene
psi	pounds per square inch
PTFE	polytetrafluoroethylene
PU	polyurethan
publ.	published, publisher(s)
publg.	publishing
publn.	publication
PVAc	polyvinyl acetate
PV alc.	polyvinyl alcohol
PVB	polyvinyl butyral
PVC	polyvinyl chloride
PVC/Ac	polyvinyl chloride-acetate
PVdC	polyvinylidene chloride
PVP	poly(vinylpyrrolidone)
QPCS	Queen's Printer & Controller of Stationery
qual.	qualitative(ly)
quant.	quantitative(ly)
qt.	quart(s)
r.	Roentgen unit(s)
R&D	Research and Development
RC	regenerated cellulose
redg.	reducing
redn.	reduction
redox	oxidation-reduction
ref.	reference(s)
rel.	relative(ly)
rep	roentgen equivalent(s) physical
Rep.	Republic
rept.	report
resp.	respective(ly)
rev.	review
revd.	reviewed
revg.	reviewing
R_f	chromatographic constant; ratio of solute: solvent travel distances
RH	relative humidity
Rom.	Romanian
rpm	revolution(s) per minute
Russ.	Russian
SA.	Societe anonyme, Sociedad anonima, spolek aktiovy, etc.
sapon.	saponification
sapond.	saponified
sapong.	saponifying
SARL.	Societe a responsabilite limitee
sat.	saturate
satd.	saturated
satg.	saturating
satn.	saturation
Scand.	Scandinavia(n)
sci.	science, scientific(ally)
SE	Southeast, southeastern
sec.	second(s)
sec-	secondary
sect.	section [in journals]
Sec'y.	Secretary
sep.	separate
sepd.	separated
sepg.	separating
sepn.	separation
Sept.	September
ser.	series
simult.	simultaneous(ly)
SLA	Special Libraries Assocn.
Slovak.	Slovakian
Soc.	Society, sociedad, etc.
sol.	soluble
soln.	solution
soly.	solubility
sp.	species [singular only!]; specific [denoting a physical constant or property]
SpA.	Societa per Azioni, Sociedade por Accoes
Span.	Spanish
spec.	specification
spectry.	spectroscopy, spectrophotometry
sp.gr.	specific gravity
spont.	spontaneous(ly)
spp.	species [plural]
sq.cm.	square centimeter(s)
S.-R.	degree(s) Schopper-Riegler [freeness]
SSL	spent sulfite liquor
statist.	statistical(ly), statistics
std.	standard
stdn.	standardization
sum.	summary, summaries
suppl.	supplement [noun only!]
supt.	superintendent
SW	Southwest, southwestern
Swed.	Sweden, Swedish
sym.	symmetrical(ly)
symp.	symposium
synt.	synthesis, synthetic
t.	ton(s)
TAGA	Technical Assocn. of the Graphic Arts
TAPPI	Technical Assocn. of the Pulp & Paper Industry
Tappi	Journal of TAPPI
tech.	technical(ly)
technol.	technological(ly); technology
temp.	temperature
tert-	tertiary
titrd.	titrated
titrg.	titrating
titrn.	titration
theoret.	theoretical(ly)
TLC	thin-layer chromatography
TNII	Tsentralnyi Nauchno-Issle-dovatel'skii Institut [Central Research Institute]
TOC	total organic carbon
transl.	translation, translator(s), translated
trd.	treated
trg.	treating
trmt.	treatment
UF	urea-formaldehyde
Ukr.	Ukrainia(n)
UN	United Nations
Univ.	University
U.S.	United States
U.S.A.	United States of America
USSR	Union of Soviet Socialist Republics
UV	ultraviolet
v.	volt(s)
VCI	volatile corrosion inhibitor
VEB.	Volkseigener Betrieb
vert.	vertical(ly)
viscy.	viscosity
viz.	videlicet: namely
VNII	Vsesoyuznyi Nauchno-Issle-dovatel'skii Institut [All-Union Research Institute]
vol.	volume
VPI	vapor-phase inhibitor
vs.	versus: against
w.	watt(s)
w.-hr.	watt-hour(s)
Wis.	Wisconsin
WRV	water retention value
wt.	weight
WV	water vapor
yr.	year(s)

PREFACE

This bibliography is Supplement II to Bibliographic Series No. 185, Flame-proofing, which was published in 1965. It covers the literature from the end of 1964 through May, 1971.

The Abstract Bulletin of The Institute of Paper Chemistry has been searched from Vol. 35, no. 6 (February, 1965) through Vol. 42, no. 7 (Jan., 1972) and the TAPPI Bibliography from 1963 through 1970.

The bibliography is divided into nine broad subjects. They are Paper, Board, Wood, Textiles, Plastics, Coatings, Testing, Synthesis, and General; and the abstracts have been subdivided accordingly. When an abstract covers applications to several of the above, including paper, the paper application is given precedence and the abstract is classified therein. Where other applications overlap, precedence is determined as follows: Paper, Board, Wood, Textiles, and Plastics; with the exception that paper, board, wood and textile coatings are found under Coatings. Board is generally interpreted to be fiber and pulp board rather than lumber which is grouped under Wood. The regenerated celluloses are classified under Textiles when they may be considered to be fibers or fabrics and under Plastics when used as resins and films. The subject groups Testing and Synthesis contain abstracts covering testing procedures for evaluation of flame resistance of a proofed material and syntheses of organic flame retardants, respectively. The General section contains abstracts of flameproofing compositions for which specific applications to one of the above headings are not apparent. In addition, abstracts covering theoretical and general reviews of flameproofing are grouped under General.

A general discussion of flameproofing was incorporated into the introduction of the 1959 bibliography.

Photocopies of original articles cited in ABIPC abstracts may be obtained from the Library of The Institute of Paper Chemistry, except where marked abstract only. Copies of patents should be ordered from the patent office of the country of origin.

FLAMEPROOFING

GENERAL

1. Akita, K.; Kase, M. Determination of kinetic parameters for pyrolysis of cellulose and cellulose treated with ammonium phosphate by differential thermal analysis and thermal gravimetric analysis. J. Polymer Sci. (A-1:Polymer Chem.) 5, no. 4:833-48(April, 1967); ABIPC 38:A3358.

Activation energy (E), preexponential factor [k(sub o)], and reaction order (n) for the pyrolysis of alpha-cellulose and cellulose modified with monoammonium phosphate were detd. by means of thermal gravimetric and differential thermal analyses. The flg. values were obtained: E = 53.5 kcal./mole, k(sub o) = 10 exp(18.8 log 10)/min., n = 1 for alpha-cellulose and E = 32 kcal./mole, k(sub o) = 10 exp(12 log 10)/min., and n = 1 for modified cellulose. A new differential thermal anal. theory (math. trmt.) was also devd. This theory, in which it is concluded that the peak value of the differential thermal anal. curve coincides with the max. rate of reaction, may be used not only for the present work but is gen. applicable to differential thermal anal. studies. Exptl. procedures and theory are described in detail.

2. Allgemeine Papier-Rundschau. Chemical products for beater addition. Allg. Papier-Rundschau no. 3:52, 54, 56, 58-64(Jan. 20, 1969); Ger.; ABIPC 40:A1900.

Chem. additives for the pmkg. process (wet-strength, flame-retarding, resin-pptg. and -fixing agents, etc.) are listed by trade name along with mfr., chem. cpn., and specific uses.

3. Arnold, W. O., Jr.; Harpold, E. C. Fire-resistant molding composition. Can. pat. 845,234(June 23, 1970); ABIPC 41:A6785.

A fire-resistant molding cpn. in pulverulent form for making insulated elec. boxes comprises PF resin, org. fibers such as sisal and cotton, inorg. fibers such as asbestos, LC filler such as wood flour and bark, PVC, Sb trioxide, and lubricant.

4. Back, E. L. Thermal auto-crosslinking in cellulose material. Pulp Paper Mag. Can. 68, no. 4:T165-71(April, 1967); ABIPC 38:A1771.

A rev. is given of model expts. on the auto-cross-linking of cellulose and hemicellulose chains, occurring in heat trmt. and as the primary step in cellulose pyrolysis. Cross-linking reduces the swellability of the cellulose matl. in softeners, such as water; hence it can be measured by wet strength and dimensional stability parameters. The homogeneity of the reactions within the temp. range 70-350 C. is shown by Arrhenius diagrams for a few such parameters. The cross-linking reaction is catalyzed at a low pH in the cellulose matl. and also by metal ions with a high redox potential. Preoxidn. of the matl. with periodate, which introduces dialdehyde groups, speeds the auto-cross-linking reaction. It is proposed that hemiacetal bridges are formed where carbonyl groups and radicals have devd. by heat and oxidn. in the cellulose chain. The cross-linking is then the velocity-detg. reaction. The effect of the auto-cross-linking reaction on the thermal softening of cellulose, esp. in the glass transition region of 200-300 C., is exemplified. Catalysis of cross-linking reactions is suggested as the primary mechanism of many fire retardants for cellulose.

5. Borg-Warner Corp. Cellulosic graft polymer. Brit. pat. 1,167,432 (Oct. 15, 1969); ABIPC 40:A10243.

Cellulose or a cellulose deriv. is graft copolymerized with alpha-chloro- and/or alpha-bromo-acrylonitrile in the presence of an aq. soln. of a ceric-ion-contg. catalyst such as ceric ammonium nitrate. The prod. has improved props. such as flame resistance, moisture retention, and other.

6. Dunay, M.; Jamison, S. E. Heat- and flame-resistant pyrolyzed cellular material and process of making same. U.S. pat. 3,553,132(Jan. 5, 1971); ABIPC 42:A5334.

A shaped foamed matl. formed for example from a cpn. contg. wood pulp, PVAc, Na CMC, water, an alkyl phenoxy ethoxy wetting agent, and an inorg. matl. such as boric oxide is pyrolyzed to form a carbonized heat-resistant prod. of use in pkg. and in structural applns.

7. Dynamit Nobel AG. Method of manufacturing mats or shaped elements from glass and/or mineral wool. Brit. pat. 1,144,192(March 5, 1969); ABIPC 40:A4412.

A method is provided for making a bonded fibrous mat based on glass or mineral wool which is characd. by improved resistance to smoldering. The method involves wetting the fibers with a binder comprising a PF resin, then a binder contg. a boron-contg. cpd. such as orthoboric acid, or alternatively, wetting the fibers with a binder cpn. contg. both the PF resin and the boron-contg. cpd., and subsequently hardening the binder without foaming. No colloidal silicic acid is present in the binder.

8. Gaeth, R.; Schmitt, B.; Breu, R. Production of fireproofing sheets. Can. pat. 698,529(Nov. 24, 1964); ABIPC 35:A6786.

This process for making fireproof sheets of inorg. fibers is similar to that described in Brit. pat. 933,410; see Abstr. No. 19 in Biblio. Series No. 185, Suppl. I, Flameproofing, 1965.

9. Glycerine Producers' Assocn. Physical properties of glycerine and its solutions. Chemical properties and derivatives of glycerine. Uses of glycerine. N.Y., The Assocn., 1963, 1964?, 1965:20 + 27 + 28 p.; ABIPC 36:A6518.

This ser. of 3 pamphlets brings up to date the data originally compiled in A.C.S. Monograph no. 17 by C. S. Miner and N. N. Dalton, titled ''Glycerol'' (N.Y., Reinhold Publ. Co., c1953), now out of print. Among applns. of glycerol noted in the 3d pamphlet are formulations of flameproofing and sizing agents. Of special interest is the use of glycerol in the paper, vegetable parchment, cellophane, pkg., wood, and graphic arts inds. 73 + 141 ref.

10. Hendrix, J. E. Thermal degradation of cellulose and related carbo-hydrates in the presence of selected organic phosphates. Ph.D. Thesis. Clemson Univ., 1970:113 p. [Univ. Microfilms, Ann Arbor, Mich.]; Diss. Abstr. 31, no. 6:3320B(Dec., 1970); ABIPC 42:A2340.

The effects of phenyl phosphates on the pyrolysis of cotton cellulose were investigated to obtain information about the interactions of flame retardants with cellulose during burning. Thermal degradations of cellulose-phenyl phosphate mixts. proceeded endothermically below 300 C. through formation of cellulose phosphate and subsequent ester pyrolysis to yield dehydrated cellulose chars. Selected nitrogenous bases reacted with triphenylphosphate (TPP) during pyrolysis to yield complex phosphoramides which formed esters with cellulose in higher yield and at lower temps. than did TPP alone. The addn. of nitrogenous bases increased the flame retardancy of cellulose. This occurred because the phosphoramides formed during the pyrolysis reacted more completely with the cellulose OH groups than did TPP. The pyrolyses of cellulose model cpds. in mixts. with phenyl phosphates were also investigated. These studies gave added support to interpretations of data obtained from pyrolyses of trd. cotton cellulose, and showed that levoglucosan is not a major intermediate in the pyrolysis of cellulose trd. with phenyl phosphates, phosphoramides, or systems capable of forming phosphoramides.

11. Hindersinn, R. R.; Wagner, G. M. Fire retardancy [of polymers]. Encyl. Polym. Sci. Technol. 7:1-64(1967); Engl.; CA 69:A10723.

A discn. of flammability of polymers, incl. theory of the burning process, test methods, and prodn. of fire-retardant polymers. Com. fire-retardant polymers, incl. their economic factors and toxicity, are described, as are methods of imparting fire retardancy to cellulose. 234 ref.

12. Hoyt, C. H.; Goheen, D. W. Polymeric products [from lignin]. Lignins (Wiley-Interscience), p. 833-65(1971); ABIPC 42:A3628.

The prepn., prodn., and potential com. uses of lignin-derived ind. chemicals are revd., incl. flame retardants. 132 ref.

13. Kasem, M. A.; Richards, H. R.; Walker, C. C. Preparation and characterization of phosphorus-nitrogen polymers for flameproofing cellulose. I. Polymers of tetrakis(hydroxymethyl)phosphonium chloride (THPC) and amines. J. Appl. Polym. Sci. 15, no. 9:2237-43(1971); CA 76:A15655.

14. Kepple, C. G.; Martello, N. E.; Zeise, C. L., Jr. Flexible flame retardant foil-clad laminates. U.S. pat. 3,526,573(Sept. 1, 1970); ABIPC 41:A6921.

A printed circuit consists of a substrate of flexible fibrous matl. such as paper, a smooth coating of a flame-retardant synt. resin permeating the substrate, a resinous adhesive on one surface of the substrate, and a metal foil (forming the circuit) embedded in the adhesive. Either the adhesive or the resin, or both, contains a satd. polyhydric alc. resinous reaction prod. The synt. resin coating can be an epoxy resin and the adhesive can be a phenolic nitrile rubber cpn.

15. Kepple, C. G.; Martello, N. E.; Zeise, C. L., Jr. Flexible flame retardant foil-clad laminates and method of manufacture. Can. pat. 804,578 (Jan. 21, 1969); ABIPC 40:A2637.

A flexible flame-retardant laminate of use in making printed circuits comprises a single sheet of fibrous matl. (e.g., paper, glass cloth, etc.) impregnated and coated with a pore-free coating of a resin contg. a Cl and an Sb cpd., a resinous adhesive on at least one side of the sheet, and a metal foil adherently bonded by the resinous adhesive to the fibrous matl. The impregnating resin can be a chlorendic alkyd resin contg. Sb oxide.

16. Krebs, H. Wood-chip moldings. Holz Roh-Werkstoff 25, no. 10:383-92 (Oct., 1967); Ger.; ABIPC 38:A7532.

The devt. of processes, particularly in Germany, for the prodn. of wood-chip molded prods., with and without the use of a binder, is revd. Covered are the additives (hardeners, flameproofing chemicals, insecticides, fungicides, waxes, dyes) commonly used in such prods., the construction of the pressing molds, the various gen. types of prods. formed, the types of chips used in mfg. the various prods., the surface coating and laminating of the molded prods., and the swelling and absorption props. and screw- and nail-holding strength of the finished prods. 24 ref.

17. Kryazhev, Y. G.; Polyakov, A. I.; Trofimov, B. A.; Petrinska, V. B.; Il'ina, L. A.; Nikitin, V. M. Method for producing non-flammable cellulosic materials. USSR pat. 268,643; Publ. Otkryt. Izobret. 47, no. 14:69(April 10, 1970); CA 73:A100230; ABIPC 41:A5548.

The flame resistance and strength of cellulosic matls. are increased and the process of flameproofing is intensified by using vinyl esters of P acids as the P-contg. cpds.

18. Lincrusta S.A. Flame-resistant container. Fr. pat. 1,422,337(Nov. 15, 1965); ABIPC 38:A7092.

A fiber drum or the like is rendered flame resistant through incorporation of an outer sidewall layer consisting of alternate plies of kraft paper and Al foil. In addn., the top and/or the bottom are provided with a hole covered by a matl. with a low melting point, such as tin. When the container encounters elevated temps., the tin melts, permitting the release of pressure built up in the container. Such a container can withstand temps. of up to 800 C. for 15 to 20 min.

19. Lipska, A. E. Pyrolysis of cellulosic and synthetic materials in a fire environment. U.S. Naval Radiological Defense Lab. Rept. TR-1113 [Springfield, Va., CFSTI, AD 645 858]:33 p.(Dec. 14, 1966); ABIPC 38:A2572.

The thermal degradation of cellulosic and synt. (e.g., PE) matls. is revd. Included are various studies on the thermal degradation of polymers, methods of heating and analg. the decpn. prods., and current theories on the mechanisms of pyrolysis of these matls. These include pyrolytic degradation at low and high temps., and the effect of ash content and oxidg. agent on thermal degradation. In addn., fire retardants and toxic cpds. resulting from the thermal degradation are discussed. Recommendations are made for further exptl. study leading toward a better understanding of the pyrolytic processes involved in the pyrolysis of org. fuels. 101 ref.

20. Lipska, A. E. Synergistic effect of benzhydrylation-iodination on the flammability of alpha-cellulose. San Francisco, U.S. Naval Radiol. Defense Lab. [Final Rept. Contract no. DAHC20-67-C-0149] May, 1969:22 p. [AD701959; avail. from CFSTI]; ABIPC 41:A2981.

Cellulose samples (a blend of 25% southern pine sulfite pulp and 75% sweet-gum sulfate pulp) were subjected to various degrees of iodination, benzhydrylation, and benzhydrylation fld. by iodination. The effect of these trmts. on crysty., rate of thermal degradation, char prodn., and pyrolysis prods. was investigated. Results indicated that in gen. the crysty. index varies inversely with the percent of substitution, rate of wt. loss, and amt. of residual char. Although the rates of wt. loss of the substituted samples increased from 0.3%/min. to as high as 108%/min. dep. on the type and percent of substitution, the overall wt. loss pattern of the trd. cellulose was similar to that of the untrd. samples. Of the three types of retardants examd., I was the best flame retardant in that the residual char increased by a large factor for a given increase in rate. The addn. of benzhydryl groups to the iodinated sample seemed to decrease rather than increase the char prodg. ability. All three trmts. reduced the no. of degradation prods. of samples with mol.wt. lower than 150; untrd. cellulose gave 59 components whereas the substituted cellulose gave five major cpds.; water, acetic acid, furfural, 5-methyl-2-furfuraldehyde, and 1,5-anhydro-2,3-deoxy-beta-D-pent-2-eno-furanose. Water and the furanose deriv. were the major components.

21. Lipska, A. E.; McCasland, G. E. Synergistic effect of benzhydrylation and iodination on the flammability of alpha-cellulose. J. Appl. Polym. Sci. 15, no. 2:419-35(1971); CA 75:A89411.

22. MacKay, G. D. M. Mechanism of thermal degradation of cellulose: a review of the literature. Can. Dept. Forestry Publ. no. 1201:20 p.(1967); ABIPC 39:A85.

A detailed account and critical assessment is given of research on the thermal degradation of cellulose. Early and current theories of flameproofing are described and discussed in relation to theories of thermal degradation. The contributions of the major current exptl. approaches to the study of thermal degradation of cellulosic matls. are described, incl. thermal gravimetric and differential thermal analyses, IR spectroscopy, gas chromat., paper chromat., and other forms of fraction anal. The productivity of each of these approaches in characg. the phenomena involved and providing data for theoret. interpretation is assessed. Particular attention is given to anal. by the thermal gravimetric and differential thermal techniques since these have been particularly useful in classifying the actions of fire retardants and identifying the roles that they play in modifying the processes involved in thermal degradation. 62 ref.

23. Oertel, G.; Holtschmidt, H.; Carl, W. Alkoxymethylamide derivatives of ester and/or amides of acids of phosphorus. Brit. pat. 1,192,862(May 20, 1970); ABIPC 41:A5575.

Fibrous matls. are rendered flameproof by trmt. with alkoxymethylamide derivs. of esters and/or amides of acids of phosphorus. A typical cpd. provided by the invention is obtained by reaction of diallyl phosphite with methoxymethyl-isocyanate.

24. Papierfabrik Wilhelmstal Wilhelm Ernst GmbH. Apparatus for manufacture
of heat-insulating material. Brit. pat. 1,100,982(Jan. 31, 1968); ABIPC 39:A3411.

This app. pulverizes newsprint, then impregnates the pulverized matl. with
a precise amt. of flameproofing substance incl. boric acid.

25. Petrov, K. A.; Andreev, L. N.; Sopikova, I. I. Flame-resistant
cellulosic materials. USSR pat. 215,483(Filed Aug. 13, 1965); Izobret. no.
13:79(1968); Russ.; ABIPC 39:A3176.

Flame resistance and ion-exchange props. are imparted simult. to cellulosic
matls. through phosphorylation with a mixt. of monoalkyl (aryl) phosphinic acid
and urea.

26. Ranney, M. W. Fire retardant building products and coatings. Park
Ridge, N. J., Noyes Data Corp. 1970:186 p.; CA 73:A68056.

27. Rogovin, Z. A. Basic trends in technological development of the
chemical fiber industry. Zh. Vses. Khim. Obshchestva im. D. I. Mendeleeva
11, no. 6:602-11(1966); Russ.; ABIPC 38:A139.

In analg. the devt. of the synt. and artificial fiber ind. during the past
30 yr., and the more recent achievements in research and technol., two essential
trends can be observed, viz. technol. improvements in the mfg. processes of mass-
prodn. fibers, such as CA, polycaprolactam, polyamide, and PAN fibers; and,
through the cooperation of research insts. and ind., the prodn., on a limited
scale of special-purpose fibers, such as fibers resistant to high temps., and
to chemicals, flameproof and nonmelting fibers, fibers with ion-exchange props.,
semiconductor fibers, and biol. active fibers. These two basic trends are
discussed, and some of the new mfg. processes for fibers produced on a large
scale, and the characs. of some special-purpose fibers are described.

28. Rogovin, Z. A. Chemical conversions and modifications of cellulose.
Moscow, 'Khimiya,' 1967:174 p.; Russ.; ABIPC 39:A916.

This book summarizes the results of research, carried out within the past
decade at the Textile Inst. in Moscow under the direction of the author, the
purpose of which was to study the chem. reactions of cellulose and the possibilities
of modifying its props. by the appln. of these reactions so as to produce new
cellulosic matls. for the textile, pulp and paper, plastics, and other inds.
The subject is discussed in the flg. four chapters: I. Basic methods for the
synt. of cellulose derivs. (through substitution of the H atom in OH groups,
through selective oxidn. of the OH groups, through replacement of the OH groups
by nucleophilic substitution, through the synt. of anhydro-derivs., through the
introduction of new functional groups by electrophilic substitution, through the
addn. of free radicals, etc.). II. Reactions of synt. polymer chemistry used
for chem. modification of cellulose (graft copolymerization of cellulose by
various methods). III. Introduction of functional groups into the cellulose
mol. (COOH, CO, CHO, sulfate and sulfonic, P-contg. groups, halogens, aliphatic
and aromatic amino groups, nitrile groups, phenyl, SH, and epoxy groups, double
and triple bonds, groups contg. Si, N-contg. heterocycles, complex-forming groups,
and organo-metallic groups). IV. New cellulosic matls. (fabrics from modified

regenerated cellulose fibers, modified CA prods., various flame-resistant prods., prods. resistant to biol. degradation or to light, waterproof prods., thermo-plastics, ion exchangers, complexons, and medicinals). 242 ref.

29. Rogovin, Z. A. Novel methods of modifying cellulose properties. Magyar Textiltech. 16, no. 12:551-5(Dec., 1964); Hung.; ABIPC 35:A6190.

This rev. of research work, based partly on the author's studies, discusses changes in cellulose structure, conformation, and chem. cpn., the synt. of cel-lulose stereoisomers, and related topics. A tabular sum. is given of attainable modifications in cellulose characs. (e.g., flameproofing, rotproofing, crease-proofing, waterproofing, and similar trmts.).

30. Rogovin, Z. A.; Tyuganova, M. A.; Predvoditelev, D. A.; Abramov, M. V. Method of obtaining modified cellulosic materials. USSR pat. 183,322(Filed April 4, 1963); Publ. Izobret. no. 13:56(1966); ABIPC 37:A6717.

Aldehyde groups are introduced into cellulose through oxidn., and then, to make the oxidized cellulosic matl. flame resistant, this matl. is trd. with dimethyl phosphite.

31. Schabert, R. Process for the manufacture of difficultly combustible fibrous mats. Ger. pat. 1,189,516(Nov. 18, 1965); ABIPC 37:A493.

A process for the mfr. of noncombustible fibrous mats of use, e.g., as air filters, involves impregnating a fibrous fleece consisting of 10 to 70% (by wt.) of a plasticizable Cl-contg. noncombustible fiber (such as PVC fiber) and 90 to 30% of a combustible fiber (such as CDA fiber) with an Sb oxide-contg. plasticizer nonreactive at room temp. (such as the butyl amide of benzenesulfonic acid) such that a total amt. of 5-20% (based on fiber wt.) is absorbed. Flg. impregnation, the fleece is crimped and subjected to a heat trmt.

32. Shafizadeh, F. Pyrolysis and combustion of cellulosic materials. Adv. Carbohyd. Chem. 23:419-74(1968); ABIPC 39:A8396.

This lit. rev. deals with the primary and secondary reactions and reaction prods. of cellulosic fuels on combustion, incl. reaction mechanisms and kinetics, thermal anal., flameproofing theories and cpds., and the interaction of flame retardants. 119 ref.

33. Thaler, H. J. Fireproof cellulosic materials. Belg. pat. 636,515 (Dec. 16, 1963); ABIPC 35:A6820.

An aq. slurry contg. cellulosic fibers (e.g., wood fibers) and Si dioxide is adjusted to pH 6.8-8.3 to form flocculent silicic acid gel ppts., which deposit on the fibers to yield a fireproof prod.

34. Thaler, H. J. Process for the manufacture of flame resistant wood fibers. Fr. pat. 1,429,099(Jan. 10, 1966); ABIPC 38:A4126.

A process for flameproofing a suspension of wood fibers by trmt. with a silicate (water glass) soln. without causing the pptn. of the silicate, is based

on the observation that when the pH of a silicate soln. is lowered rapidly to
below 6 (to 5-3.2) at a low temp., the silicate remains for some time in soln.
When such a clear soln. at a low pH is added to an aq. suspension of fibers, the
silicate is deposited on the fibers without pptg. in the soln. and hence without
losses with waste water.

35. Tsuchiya, Y.; Sumi, K. Thermal decomposition products of cellulose.
J. Appl. Polymer Sci. 14, no. 8:2003-13(Aug., 1970); ABIPC 41:A8148.

Untrd. and flame retardant-trd. cellulose were thermally decpd. under vacuum
and the prods. were anald. by gas chromat. An unidentified prod. with a retention
index of 2270 (between 5-methylfurfural and 5-hydroxymethylfurfural), alpha- and
beta-D-glucose, and a group of dimers that have not been reported previously,
were found. Identification of this unknown prod. should assist in studies on the
thermal decpn. of cellulose and further the understanding of the mechanism of
flame retardancy.

36. Turner, J. H. W.; Krug, P. Bleaching of wood pulp with thiourea
dioxide and zinc sulfate. U.S. pat. 3,481,828(Dec. 2, 1969); ABIPC 41:A1835.

A process for bleaching wood pulp comprises bleaching the pulp in a cpn.
contg. 0.2-1.0% thiourea dioxide and 1-5% zinc sulfate based on the wt. of dry
wood substance in the pulp. The bleaching process can be carried out simult.
with a fire-retardant trmt. with borates or phosphates.

37. Usmanov, K. U.; Azizov, U. A.; Sadykov, M. U. Radiation grafting of
vinyl monomers on cellulose in the vapor phase. Radiats. Khim. Polim. Mater.,
Simp., Moscow 1964:153-7(publ. 1966); Russ.; ABIPC 38:A2584.

Graft copolymerization of cellulose (cotton fibers and fabrics) with monomer
vapors was undertaken in an attempt to prevent the formation of large amts. of
the homopolymers, observed when solns. of the monomers are used. The monomers
in this study were acrylonitrile, 2-vinylpyridine, and vinylidene chloride, which
impart to cellulose biol. resistance, dyeability with acid dyes, and flame resistance, resp. The vapors of the monomers were passed continuously through cellulose irradiated with gamma-rays at a rate of 70 rad/sec. Since it was observed
that the copolymerization rate increased in the presence of moisture, cellulose
was satd. with WV. The vapor carrier was N. In the case of acrylonitrile, the
amt. of the homopolymer did not exceed 1-3%, based on cellulose wt. (10-20% of
grafted monomer), and at a wt. increment of less than 8%, the modified cellulose
had a biol. resistance equal to that attained at 15% increment when the reaction
is carried out in the liquid phase. This, evidently, indicates a more uniform
distribution of the grafted chains. Similarly good results were obtained with
vinylpyridine. Copolymerization with vinylidene chloride was less successful,
as considerable amts. of the homopolymer were formed, and significant loss of
the mech. strength of the fibers was observed (there was no loss with the other
two monomers).

38. Valetdinov, R. K.; Kuznetsov, E. V.; Mikheeva, T. Y.; Gumarova, R. Z.
Method of flameproofing cellulosic materials. USSR pat. 230,774(Filed Jan. 31,
1966); Izobret. no. 35:10(1968); ABIPC 40:A464.

A flameproofing trmt. which does not cause an undue loss of mech. strength of cellulosic matls. consists in impregnation of such matls., at pH 6-7, with a soln. contg. tetramethylolphosphonium hydroxide and a N-contg. monomer, e.g., urea or melamine. The impregnated matl. is then heat-cured.

39. Vol'f, L. A.; Meos, A. I. Methods for obtaining fibers with special properties. Khim. Volokna 11, no. 1:13-16(1969); Russ.; ABIPC 41:A1059.

The chem. modification of PV alc. and cellulose fibers to give fibers with special props., such as semiconducting fibers, ion-exchange fibers, electron-exchange fibers, biologically active fibers (bactericidal and in some cases, viricidal) and other fibers with special props. (noncombustible or fireproof, water repellent, and others) is discussed. 23 ref.

40. Weiner, J.; Byrne, J. Flameproofing. Appleton, Wis., IPC [Bibl. Ser. no. 185] Suppl. I, 1965:121 p.; ABIPC 36:A6519.

This suppl. covers the pertinent lit. from the end of 1958 to the end of 1964. 689 ref.

41. Willey, G. S. Fire-resistant plaster product. U.S. pat. 3,454,456 (July 8, 1969); ABIPC 40:A4424.

A set calcined gypsum cast of improved fire rating, suitable as a core for gypsum wallboard comprises unexpanded vermiculite of specified particle sizes selected so as to impart to the cast a linear contraction of no more than 0.2% after being heated and substantially no thickness expansion after being cooled. At least about 0.1% by wt. of mineral fibers and boric acid may also be included.

BOARD

42. Abe, H.; Fukui, Y.; Hirata, T. Study on fireproofing chemicals. (1) Mixtures of phosphorus, halogen, and boron compounds. (Report I). Bull. Govt. Forest Expt. Sta. (Tokyo) no. 194:127-53(Sept., 1966); Jap.; ABIPC 38:A4259.

Wood of sugi (Cryptomeria japonica) was trd. with 27 solns. contg. varying proportions of diammonium phosphate, ammonium bromide, and boric acid. From the results of combustion tests, the mechanisms of action of each component were deduced, and optimum flameproofing formulations were detd. which would, however, vary with the type of substrate to be trd. (plywood, fiberboard). The presence of boric acid seemed unnecessary, if not harmful under certain conditions. Of the other 2 cpds., the phosphate exerted its flame-retardant effect much longer than the bromide.

43. Abitibi Paper Co. Ltd. Flame-retardant particle board. Brit. pat. 1,069,363(May 17, 1967); ABIPC 38:A5661.

The wood flakes used in making the board are pretrd. with a soln. contg. a borate such as Na tetraborate, together with a strong mineral acid such as HCl.

44. Adomshick, G. J.; Quinn, R. G. Decorative non-combustible ceiling. Can. pat. 811,361(April 29, 1969); ABIPC 40:A6338.

A ceiling tile is formed by pmkg. methods from a furnish incl. 80-88% asbestos fibers, 10-15% thermoplastic resin such as PVC, and 2-5% whitening agent. After the furnish is sheeted out, it is embossed with a desired pattern.

45. Alexander, W. O. Fireproof heat-insulating materials. Brit. pat. 1,089,879(Nov. 8, 1967); ABIPC 39:A1619.

A flameproof heat-insulating cpn. of use in making board comprises a mixt. of finely divided low-d. refractory matl. such as perlite, fibrous refractory matl. such as asbestos, man-made org. fiber such as an acrylic resin fiber, and a Na silicate binding agent.

46. Barbier, M. Process for the manufacture of flame-resistant panels. Fr. pat. 1,349,907(Dec. 16, 1963); ABIPC 36:A6064.

To mfr. flame-resistant wood-particle boards (or boards from other cellulosic particulate matls., e.g., flax waste), the particles are mixed with 9-15% (based on dry wt.) UF binder contg. a hardening agent, and the mixt. is trd. prior to hot-pressing with a mixt. of borocalcite and boric acid, the amt. of the flame-proofing agent being less than 50% of the resin (the ratio of its two components can vary). Alternatively, the flameproofing agent can be added to the binder.

47. Barker, P. W.; Tew, H. J.; Watkins, R. C. Fire retardant laminate. Can. pat. 822,068(Sept. 2, 1969); ABIPC 40:A9541.

A composite laminated roofing matl. consists of an elastomeric sheet and an outer sheet contg. fire-retarding matl. such as perchloropentacyclodecane. The outer layer can be an asbestos fiber matl.

48. Bauer, D. R. Fire-resistant building board and process. U.S. pat. 3,300,372(Jan. 24, 1967); ABIPC 38:A797.

A fire-resistant building board is formed from a furnish incl. a major portion of synt. mineral fibers, a minor portion of LC fibers, 5-15% starch, 10-30% clay, 0.5-4.0% size, and 0.2-2.25% of a cationic surface-active agent such as cationic starch.

49. Baum, G. A.; Gottlieb, J. B. Flame-resistant wood particle board. Can. pat. 844,027(June 9, 1970); ABIPC 41:A5911.

A process for making flame-resistant particle board comprises coating the wood particles with a thermally-unstable Cl-contg. matl. (e.g., PVC) and with at least one Sb cpd. such as Sb trioxide, separately coating the particles with adhesive, forming the particles into a board mat, and compressing and curing.

50. Bescher, R. H. Method of adding fire retardant chemicals to a fiber board while on the forming wire. U.S. pat. 3,271,238(Sept. 6, 1966); ABIPC 37:A6999.

A method for adding fire-retardant chemicals to fiberboard involves flooding the wet mat on the fourdrinier wire (after the removal of a major portion of the water) with a soln. of the chemicals, applg. suction to draw the soln. through the mat so that the fibers take up the desired amt. of retardant, and collecting for reuse the soln. which passes completely through the mat. The soln. can be an aq. soln. of ammonium hydrogen phosphate, ammonium sulfate, and NaF.

51. Blunt, G. V. D. Method of forming fire-retardant sheet material. Brit. pat. 1,215,580(Dec. 9, 1970); ABIPC 42:A5322.

A method of making fire-retardant particle board comprises mixing diammonium phosphate and/or monoammonium phosphate and ammonium sulfate with wood particles, separately mixing in a binder resin, and pressing the matl. to form the desired boards.

52. Board Manufacture. Sodium silicate in the manufacture of wallboard. Board Mfr. 11, no. 10:118-19(Oct., 1968); Engl.; ABIPC 39:A8647.

The use of Na silicate in the mfr. of wallboard is revd. It has the advantages of prodg. strong bonds between the substrate particles, is inexpensive, and has excellent fire-resistant props. 26 ref.

53. Bremmer, B. J.; Sonnabend, L. F. Process for impregnating wood and products thereof. U.S. pat. 3,519,476(July 7, 1970); ABIPC 41:A7924.

Wood and hardboard and the like are dimensionally stabilized and flame-proofed by impregnating the woody matl. with a prod. obtained by reacting a phenol and ammonia or urea or an amine with an aldehyde such as HCHO and adding an acid to the reaction mixt., then heating the impregnated matl. The heat trmt. can be carried out in the presence of excess ammonia or urea.

54. Brovkina, V. I.; Leonovich, A. A.; Solechnik, N. Y. Changes in the carbohydrate complex and durability of constructional fiberboards. Izv. VUZ, Lesnoi Zh. 13, no. 3:93-6(1970); Russ.; ABIPC 41:A8356.

Considering that the durability of fiberboards is detd. primarily by the state of the ''reinforcing'' component, i.e., cellulose, a study was made of the durability of boards contg. flameproofing additives (phosphoric acid, urea, and dicyandiamide in a wt. ratio 9.5:17.4:12.2) and those not flameproofed, and of changes in the soly. of holocellulose (by fractionation with phosphoric acid) at the various stages of the board mfg. process. The boards were formed by air deposition, pressed for 4.5 min. at 180 C., and hardened at 170 C. They contained no waterproofing additives. The flameproofing cpn. was neutd. to a pH of 5 or 7. In control boards, the DP of holocellulose was reduced during hot pressing and hardening to the range 200-500. The soly. of holocellulose from flameproofed boards also was modified, the redistribution of holocellulose dispersity depending on the pH of the cpn. introduced. The gen. effect was a redn. of DP with simult. increase of the insol. fraction (DP of over 1200), and was more marked when the flameproofing cpn. had a pH of 5. The increase of the insol. residue of holo-cellulose can be attributed to cross-linking of the carbohydrate complex mols. by the flameproofing agent, the extent of which depends on the no. of free OH groups of phosphoric acid (hence is higher at pH 5). Cross-linking also increases the stability of flameproofing, by preventing leaching of the flameproofing agent. Holocellulose from flameproofed boards was characd. by the absence of fractions with DP 400-600. However, because of its content of the insol. residue which is twice that of untrd. boards, the boards should be more durable. This was confirmed by accelerated aging expts. Boards flameproofed with the acidic cpn. had higher

mech. strength and water resistance after aging than boards flameproofed with the
neutral cpn. Their slightly higher water absorption can be corrected by trmt.
with waterproofing agents.

55.   Cadotte, J. E.; Juntti, E. W. Flame-resistant mineral fiber tile.
U.S. pat. 3,248,257(April 26, 1966); ABIPC 37:A3216.

Mineral fiber ceiling tile is rendered flame-resistant by coating one
face with Na aluminate.

56.   Cadotte, J. E.; Juntti, E. W. Production of mineral tile. Can. pat.
718,592(Sept. 28, 1965); ABIPC 36:A6067.

In the mfr. of flame-resistant mineral fiber ceiling tile, the tendency of
the tile to deform when exposed to flame is counteracted by applg. Na aluminate
to one face of the tile.

57.   Chase, H. A. Process of treating composite boards with borate chemicals.
Can. pat. 836,516(March 10, 1970); ABIPC 41:A3837.

A process is provided for making fire-retardant boards from comminuted wood
and a suitable binder. The wood furnish after comminution is combined with a
fire-retardant borate such as Na borate, the furnish is dried and blended with
an acidic matl. such as boric acid together with the binder, and the furnish is
then formed and cured under heat and pressure.

58.   Chase, H. A. Process of treating composite boards with borate chemicals
produced thereby and product. U.S. pat. 3,438,847(April 15, 1969); ABIPC 40:A1706.

A process for making a flame-resistant wood-particle board comprises adding
to the particle-binder furnish a borate such as Na or K borate, forming a mat,
drying, adding an acidic matl. such as boric acid, and heating and compressing
the mat.

59.   Chemical Engineering. Paper houses woo buyers. Chem. Eng. 76, no.
19:76, 78(Sept. 8, 1969); ABIPC 40:A4799.

Inexpensive paper-based housing modules have been devd. that are claimed
to be suitable as permanent houses. The basic 400-module (400 sq. ft. of floor
space) is made of corrugated board that has been trd. to make it fire and weather
resistant. Ribbing on the inside walls and roof of the structure impart sufficient
strength so that no supplementary framework is needed. Further strength and
weather resistance are provided by cementing a glass fiber matting over the
exterior surface with a polyester resin. Several of the basic 400-modules,
can be combined to form modernistic looking structures. The developer of the
housing modules is aiming at the second-home market in the U.S. and housing for
the poor in devg. countries.

60.   Chemical Week. Recipe for housing. Chem. Week 109, no. 6:11(Aug. 11,
1971); ABIPC 42:A4803.

Low-cost housing made from chemically trd. (to resist water, fire, and
vermin) pbd. strengthened with fiberglass and polyester resins (devd. by

Universal Papertech Corp. and described previously, cf. ABIPC 41:A385) has won U.S. Federal Housing Administration approval for mortgaging.

61. Christoffersen, C.; Sorensen, K.-O. Methods of producing fire resisting wooden articles. U.S. pat. 3,498,877(March 3, 1970); ABIPC 41:A861.

This process for making a fire-resistant wood-shavings board or the like is similar to that described previously in Can. pat. 787,383; see flg. abstr.

62. Christoffersen, C.; Sorensen, K.-O. Method of producing fire-resisting wooden boards or panels. Can. pat. 787,383(June 11, 1968); ABIPC 39:A5327.

The wood pieces used in making the board (e.g., a wood shavings board or plywood) are preimpregnated with diammonium phosphate, and are then glued together under heat and pressure with the use of an adhesive comprising a synt. resin (e.g., a PF resin), kaolin, and diammonium phosphate.

63. Cotts, R. F. Felted inorganic fiber panel. Brit. pat. 1,039,763 (Aug. 24, 1966); ABIPC 38:A3210.

A rigid acoustical panel which is fire retardant and which resists shrinking consists primarily of mineral wool fibers, with up to 10% asbestos fibers, together with a starch binder. The binder includes a pulverized non-swelling clay to prevent shrinking of the panel.

64. Cotts, R. F. Fire retardant acoustical tile. Can. pat. 743,012 (Sept. 20, 1966); ABIPC 37:A7883.

This acoustical tile is similar to that described in U.S. pat. 3,103,444; see Abstr. No. 68 in Biblio. Series No. 185, Suppl. I, 1965.

65. Craig, D. W. Flameproofing of construction material. U.S. pat. 3,383,274(May 14, 1968); ABIPC 39:A3480.

A flameproof board (e.g., hardboard or wood-particle board) is made up of 3 layers, a core layer and 2 facing layers. The core layer contains rel. large wood particles, while the facing layers contain rel. fine wood particles. All layers are impregnated with crystals of an ammonium salt such as diammonium phosphate. The layers are adhered together with a binder.

66. Craig, D. W. Flameproofing of construction material. Can. pat. 759,866(May 30, 1967); ABIPC 38:A6422.

A flameproof particle board or hardboard is made up of 3 layers, with an ammonium salt distributed in optimum concns. throughout each of the layers. The salt can be diammonium phosphate.

67. Dean, R. M. Fire-resistant wallboard. U.S. pat. 3,376,147(April 2, 1968); ABIPC 39:A2538.

A fire-resistant wallboard consists essentially of gypsum, and unexpanded vermiculite and unexpanded perlite both dispersed in the gypsum. The vermiculite is present in an amt. and particle size sufficient to compensate by expansion on exposure to heat for the shrinkage of gypsum when the gypsum is exposed to heat. This expansion and contraction produces fissures which are filled by a secondary expansion of the perlite. The board can also include paper pulp or glass fibers or the like.

68.   Dean, R. M. Fire-resistant wallboard. Can. pat. 771,341(Nov. 14, 1967); ABIPC 38:A9693.

A fire-resistant wallboard is made from gypsum, unexpanded vermiculite, glass fibers, and unexpanded perlite. When the board is subjected to heat, the vermiculite tends to expand and compensate for the shrinkage of the gypsum under heat. This action produces fissures in the board. The glass fibers bridge the fissures and maintain the board strength, while the perlite tends to expand and fill the fissures to retard passage of heat.

69.   Delfour, P. Covering materials, notably for floors and walls. Can. pat. 820,855(Aug. 19, 1969); ABIPC 40:A8361.

A flame-resistant covering matl. for floors and walls comprises a sheet of asbestos paper, a layer of synt. resin coating one face of the paper, a flame-proofing substance in the resin, and an external layer of synt. fibers secured to the resin layer by a suitable adhesive. The substance incorporated in the resin as flameproofing agent can be asbestos powder, tricresylphosphate, or the like.

70.   Deppe, H. J. Improving the flame resistance of wood-particle board through inorganic surface layers. Mitt. Deut. Ges. Holzforsch. no. 56:23-6 (1969); ABIPC 42:A430.

Possibilities for improving the flame-resistance of wood-particle boards through incorporation of perlite, vermiculite, or asbestos fiber surface layers are revd. Examd. in particular is the influence of surface layer compression, binder, wood chip content, and thickness on flame resistance, ply bond adhesion, and layer strength props.

71.   Deppe, H. J. Studies on the manufacture of flame-resistant wood products. Holz Roh-Werkstoff 26, no. 8:284-7(Aug., 1968); Ger.; Transl. in Engl. (12 p.) available from IPC at copying cost; ABIPC 39:A7629; 40:A6783.

Previous studies are revd. concerning the relationships between the binder cpn. and strength props. of wood-particle boards and their flame resistance. It is shown that flameproofing agents are required for the economic mfr. of either PF or UF particle boards which meet modern stds. for flame-resistant building matls. A process involving impregnation of the wood chips with a liquid flameproofing agent is described. Indications are that the process is much more economical than processes involving the use of a flameproofing agent in the form of a powder.

72.   Deutsche Perlite GmbH. Use of swollen perlite or vermiculite and cellulose in the manufacture of light construction materials and process for the manufacture of such materials. Ger. pat. 1,239,608(Exam. copy April 27, 1967); ABIPC 39:A8204.

Construction moldings of expanded perlite or vermiculite and binder are given a high tensile strength through the addn. of cellulose fibers (particularly a waste newsprint furnish) to the molding cpn. The moldings are highly flame resistant as long as the cellulose content is rel. low (less than 35%).

73. Draganov, S. M. Fire retardants in particleboard. Proc. Symp. Particleboard (Wash. State Univ.) 2:75-121(March, 1968); ABIPC 42:A2558.

The author reviews the mechanism of wood pyrolysis and combustion, the purposes and available kinds of fire (flame resistance) tests, the problem of fume and smoke generation (and proposals for measuring it), types and characs. of com. avail. flame retardants (and their effects on wood substrates), and possible methods for flameproofing of particle boards. Special attention is paid to the pat. lit. and esp. to experience with the use of borates. The cost aspects of fire-retardant trmts. are also mentioned.

74. Duret, L. A. Manufacture of prefabricated constructional panels and products obtained. Fr. pat. 1,496,808(Aug. 28, 1967); ABIPC 40:A3525.

Constructional panels of improved weather and flame resistance are mfd. from natural fibers, such as wood fibers, sisal, bagasse, etc., or from mineral fibers, which, prior to the addn. of a thermosetting resin binder and hot pressing, are coated with a plasticizer, such as chlorinated paraffin. The fibers are trd. with the plasticizer during the shredding operation, so that penetration of the plasticizer is facilitated. The constructional boards thus obtained are also highly resistant to decay. The finished boards are aged for about 3 months before being used.

75. El'bert, A. A.; Solechnik, N. Y.; Shishkin, S. N. Method for making flame-resistant boards. USSR pat. 301,284(April 21, 1971); Otkryt. Izobret. 48, no. 14:53(1971); ABIPC 42:A7526.

Wood-particle boards are made flame-resistant by the appln. of a 30-40% soln. of K carbonate to the surface of the newly formed mat before hot pressing in amts. of 40-60 g. (o.d. wt.)/sq.m. of board surface.

76. Fairchild, W. P. Process of coating fiberboard and resulting product. U.S. pat. 3,281,252(Oct. 25, 1966); ABIPC 37:A8661.

Pressed vegetable fiber boards such as bagasse boards are flameproofed by trmt. with a soln. contg. water, a hydrophilic gum colloid produced by a bacterium of the genus Xanthomonas, and a satg. amt. of a fire-retardant agent such as boric acid.

77. Fairchild, W. P. Process of coating fiberboard and resulting product. Can. pat. 751,277(Jan. 24, 1967); ABIPC 38:A2376.

This process for forming a fire-retardant coating on building boards is similar to that described in U.S. pat. 3,281,252; see preceding abstr.

78. Formwood Ltd. Method of producing pressed chip bodies of low flammability. Brit. pat. 1,089,836(Nov. 8, 1967); ABIPC 39:A1629.

A process for prodg. particle board or the like pressed chip bodies, characd. by low flammability, involves trg. the fibrous starting matl. with an aq. soln. of fire-retardant chemicals, with the addn. of a highly reactive aldehyde such as paraformaldehyde, mixing in a suitable resin binder, and then forming and pressing in known manner.

79. Gaeth, R.; Schmitt, B.; Breu, R. Production of fireproofing boards of alkali metal silicates containing water and fibers. Brit. pat. 1,051,078 (Dec. 14, 1966); ABIPC 38:A3215.

A process for making a fire retardant board consists of adding fibers (e.g., glass fibers) to a suspension of alkali metal silicate particles in an aq. alkali metal silicate soln., forming the mixt. into a layer on a support, allowing the layer to set at a temp. below 150 C., removing the layer from the support, and completing the drying at a temp. of 50-150 C. The silicate soln. has a concn. of 25-45 deg. Be.; the suspension has a water content of 10-35% by wt. of anhydrous alkali metal silicate and a viscy. of 30-1500 cp. at 20 C. The wt. ratio of particles to water in the soln. is 1:0.6-5.0.

80. Gazelle, R. J. Radiation barrier panels. U.S. pat. 3,231,451(Jan. 25, 1966); ABIPC 37:A846.

A panel designed to serve as a barrier against fallout radiation, fire, and the like hazards consists of laminated layers of corrugated Al sheeting, fiberglass, asbestos board, neoprene, and tar paper.

81. Glaser, W. Flameproofing of inflammable natural material or synthetic polymers. Brit. pat. 1,130,776(Oct. 16, 1968); ABIPC 40:A818.

A process for flameproofing of porous matls. (e.g., wood, pbd., hardboard, synt. polymer foams, etc.) involves impregnating the matl. with a flameproofing cpd. contg. water of crystn., the matl. being in the form of a melt, and then allowing the melt to solidify in the interstices of the matl. being trd. K alum is among the preferred flameproofing cpds. used.

82. Gordienko, V. Experience in the manufacture and use of Arbolite. Lesnaya Prom. 49, no. 2:25-6(Feb., 1969); Russ.; Engl. transl. available from IPC on share-the-cost basis; ABIPC 41:A3279; 42:A3793.

The Guzeripl'sk exptl. plant for the mfr. of Arbolite has an annual prodn. capacity of 12,000 cu.m. Arbolite castings are made in the usual fashion. For the prepn. of 1 cu.m. of mix, the matls. used are: 250-400 kg. of portland cement, 180-250 kg. of wood particles, 5.6-8.0 kg. of Ca chloride, and 300-360 liters of water. Blocks and panels made from the mix have a d. of 600-750 kg./ cu.m. and a compression strength of up to 45 kg./cu.m. They withstand over 25 freeze-thaw cycles, and are decay and fire resistant. It was found that almost any kind of wood waste can be used, except oak.

83. Gorevoi, M. R.; Zdanavichyus, L. I.; Leonovich, A. A. Preparation of fire-resistant hardboards. Derevoobrabat. Prom. 18, no. 6:16(June, 1969); Russ.; ABIPC 41:A4311.

Fire-resistant hardboards are prepd. according to USSR pat. 195,626 on a pilot plant scale. The pinewood obtained from a grinder with a capacity of 20 t./24 hr. is blown into a dry cyclone. After drying to a moisture content of 10-15%, the groundwood is trd. with a mixt. neutd. to a pH of 5, consisting of 9.5 parts of orthophosphoric acid, 17.4 parts of urea, 8.2 parts of dicyandiamide, and 30 parts of water/100 parts of wood. The trd. wood is then manually placed in a wooden frame and lightly pressed. The mat so obtained is then pressed for 5 min. at 178-182 C. and 50 kg./sq.cm. The finished hardboards meet the required specs. of GOST 4598-60 after tempering.

84. Grossner, R.; Moralt, A. Wood-based molded article. Ger. pat. 1,653,254(Aug. 27, 1970); ABIPC 42:A1022.

A flame-resistant wood-particle board is characd. by at least one surface layer which is made from fines (grinder dust, sawdust) obtained from matl. (e.g., particle board) incorporating a flameproofing agent. This type of flameproofing has no adverse effects on board strength props.

85. Grossner, R.; Moralt, A., Fa. Wood-based molded article. Ger. pat. 1,903,936(Sept. 17, 1970); ABIPC 42:A3269.

The wood-particle board claimed in Ger. pat. 1,653,254 (see preceding abstr.) is further improved with respect to flame resistance through the incorporation of asbestos in the flame-resistant surface layer or layers.

86. Hallonquist, E. G.; Jaworsky, J. M.; Kassay, V. G. Fire-resistant particle board. Can. pat. 779,372(Feb. 27, 1968); ABIPC 39:A2546.

Wood-particle board bonded with UF resin is rendered fire resistant by incl. in the board-forming mixt. either monobasic ammonium phosphate or ammonium sulfate.

87. Hallonquist, E. G.; Jaworsky, J. M.; Kassay, V. G. Fire-resistant particle board containing monobasic ammonium phosphate and/or ammonium sulfate. U.S. pat. 3,415,765(Dec. 10, 1968); ABIPC 39:A9215.

Wood-particle board bonded with UF resin is rendered fire resistant by incl. in the board-making mixt. either monobasic ammonium phosphate or ammonium sulfate, in the amt. of 5-15% of the dry wt. of the wood particles.

88. Heeb, A. J.; Chalmers, E. L., II. Decorative laminate having superior fire retardant properties. U.S. pat. 3,511,748(May 12, 1970); ABIPC 41:A2832.

A decorative laminate having superior fire-retardant props. comprises the heat and pressure consolidated structure formed from the flg. laminae in the order of ascending superimposed order: an asbestos-cement board coated with PF resin, Al foil coated with an adhesive which adheres to the foil and the PF resin, a paper sheet impregnated with a MF resin, a decorative sheet impregnated with a MF resin, and a surface film of a polymer of an allyl ester of a phthalic acid.

89. Heinola Fanerfabrik Zachariassen & Co. A method for the treatment of cellulosic products and cellulosic products when treated thereby. Brit. pat. 1,174,713(Dec. 17, 1969); ABIPC 41:A1802.

A process is provided for impregnating hardboard or particle board or the like with a liquid protective matl. such as a flameproofing cpn. The hot board discharged from the forming press is passed through the nip of press rolls. At least one of the rolls is surfaced with a porous cushion of felt or the like. The liquid trg. cpn. is appl. to this porous matl. After passing through the press rolls, the board is subjected to a final heat trmt.

90. Hirata, T.; Abe, H.; Fukui, Y. Study on fireproofing chemicals. (2) Effects of various chemicals on combustion and pyrolysis of hardboard. Bull. Govt. Forest Expt. Sta. (Tokyo) no. 200:155-84(March, 1967); Jap.; ABIPC 38:A4267.

A combustion test and thermogravimetric anal. of combustion prods. were used to eval. the effect of diammonium phosphate, ammonium bromide, ammonium sulfamate, guanidine phosphate, and chlorodiphenyl on the fire behavior of hardboard (0.9 sp.gr., 60-70% lauan hardwood, rest softwood). All chemicals except chlorodiphenyl (at any degree of chlorination) exerted marked flame-proofing effects. A mixt. of boric acid and Na borate prevented afterglow, but showed a mixed mechanism of action in which the pyrolysis-accelerating and retarding effects cancelled each other. The individual performances of each salt are described in detail.

91. Homann, F., AG. Process for the manufacture of flame-resistant articles from wood fibers. Fr. pat. 1,339,026(Aug. 26, 1963); ABIPC 36:A756.

A convenient and simple method of flameproofing building boards, such as hardboards and insulation boards, is to incorporate into the fibrous web Mg sulfate in the form of a concd. soln. or a powder, the incorporation of this salt being preferably fld. by the incorporation of calcined magnesite. The two salts can be added simult. at the beater, Mg sulfate can be added first at the beater and the magnesite appl. to the partially dried web, or the two salts can be successively incorporated into the partially dried web. In all cases, the amt. of Mg salt (or salts) must be such as to bring the pH of the fibrous cpn. to 9-10. The Mg sulfate can be replaced by an equiv. amt. of Mg chloride or by a sulfate of another bivalent metal. The prods. obtained contain over 20% mineral substances and have a good flame resistance.

92. Hudson, O. Fireproof container for oxidizable materials including explosives. U.S. pat. 3,446,411(May 27, 1969); ABIPC 40:A2501.

A fireproof carton for pkg. matls. such as explosives consists of a core of corrugated pbd. laminated to fireproof facing sheets which are paper formed from a furnish of asbestos and cotton fibers.

93. Ishihara, S. Flame-retardant treatment of fiberboard. Zairyo 14, no. 143:622-7(1965); Jap.; CA 67:A65602.

To give flame-retardant props. to fiberboard, mixing of nonflammable substances, i.e., glass fibers or perlite, into fibers before forming and trmt. of wood fibers with fireproofing agents are the most suitable methods. Aq. solns. of fireproofing agents, such as diammonium phosphate, ammonium bromide, boric acid, or borates, and MeOH solns. of organophosphoric acid esters, are used for fiberboard. In many cases, the solns. are sprayed on

or soaked into semihard boards for hardboard mfr., soaking being carried out
immediately after hot-pressing because of its high d. The 2nd practical method
consists of coating of fiberboard with fire-resistant paints, thin layers of
synt. polymers, asbestos paper, or Al plate. As fireproofing agents, Zn
chloride, ammonium chloride, ammonium bromide, Mg chloride, phosphoramide,
ammonium sulfamate, diammonium phosphate, phosphonitrile chloride, tetrakis-
(hydromethyl)phosphonium chloride, tris(1-aziridinyl)phosphine oxide, tris(1-
aziridinyl)phosphine sulfide, and a urea-phosphate mixt. have been used.

94. Ishihara, S.; Maku, T. Studies on flame-retardant fiberboard. (1).
Flame retardants for hardboard based on metal oxides and/or chlorinated compounds.
Wood Res. (Kyoto) no. 34:156-73(March, 1965); Jap.; ABIPC 36:A2520.

Hardboard panels from Pinus densiflora were flameproofed by adding
various water-insol. heavy metal oxides to the pulp slurry, fld. by alum and
aq. ammonia to ppt. the oxide before the wet mat was formed and hot-pressed,
and/or by soaking or pressure-impregnating the board in org. solvent solns.
of chlorinated org. cpds., fld. by evapn. of the solvent. The trd. panels
were evald. for flame and water resistance (by detns. of afterflaming, afterglow, water-absorption rate, WV absorption, and moisture-caused thickness swelling). Among the metal oxides (Sb, Fe, Sn, Ti, Pb, Mn, Zr, Bi), only Sb oxide
(I) showed a slight flame-retardant effect at moderate (30-40%) add-ons, but
could not compare even remotely with any of the water-sol. flameproofing salts
used in control tests (e.g., borax, ammonium phosphate-sulfamate, Na silicate).
Among water-insol. chlorinated cpds. (paraffins, PCP, BHC, aniline-HCl,
ethylenediamine-HCl, PVdC, PVC-PVdC), only a highly chlorinated (70% Cl)
paraffin at rather high add-ons showed some flame retardancy. In combinations
with (I), however, nearly all chlorinated cpds. were beneficial, although
BHC, PCP, and 40%-Cl paraffin were less effective than others. Their flameproofing effect in (I) mixts. depended not only on the original Cl content but
also on the nature of the Cl bond and the volatility and amt. of the combustion
prods. evolved. Thus, aniline-HCl was more effective, despite its low (27%)
Cl content, than BHC (73% Cl) and PCP (66% Cl). Zn borate was an effective
glow suppressant in combination with (I) + chlorinated paraffin. The 70%-Cl
paraffin imparted excellent water-repellency to the hardboards. Bending
strength was better in all trd. boards than in untrd. controls, probably because
the paraffin impregnation exerted the same effect as does conventional oil
tempering.

95. Ishihara, S.; Maku, T. Studies on flame-retardant fiberboard. (2)
Performance of hardboard flameproofed with antimony trioxide plus chlorinated
compounds. Wood Res. (Kyoto) no. 37:16-31(March, 1966); Jap.; ABIPC 38:A4456.

Hardboards 35 x 35 x 0.45 cm. were impregnated with chlorinated paraffin,
vinylidene chloride resins, ethylenediamine dihydrochloride, or – for comparison –
Na pentachlorophenoxide, plus Sb oxide in each case. Std. combustion tests
indicated that 5.5% of each flame-retardant cpn. based on dry wt. was the min.
effective dose. All chlorinated cpds. were highly effective in conjunction with
Sb oxide; the penta deriv. was less so. In addn. to flame-retardant ratings,
data are given on the bending strength and water absorption of the boards, as
well as on their afterglow props. when trd. with Zn borate plus chlorinated cpds.

96. Israel, Government of. Fireproofing of bonded cellulosic and lignocellulosic articles. Brit. pat. 1,080,845(Aug. 23, 1967); ABIPC 38:A7769.

In the mfr. of bonded cellulosic matls. (i.e., laminated pbd., wood-particle board, etc.) in which a substance such as UF resin is used as the binder, fire resistance is imparted to the prod. by incorporating in the binder certain inorg. bromides and oxybromides, such as ammonium bromide and Mg oxybromide.

97. Israel, Government of. Fireproofing of lignocellulosic material. Brit. pat. 1,101,249(Jan. 31, 1968); ABIPC 39:A3525.

A process for improving the resistance of LC matls. to flame and biol. decay involves impregnating the LC matl. with a reactant capable of participating in a lignin halogenation reaction, then trg. the matl. so as to effect halogenation of the lignin. For example, the LC matl. can be impregnated with a halide or halogen, and the impregnated matl. can then be trd. with an oxidg. agent to bring about the desired reaction. In one example, NaBr is added to a wood pulp suspension, and the suspension is then mixed with Cl soln. to effect bromination of the pulp, which is then formed into board having the desired props.

98. Israel, Government of. Flameproofing of cellulosic and lignocellulosic materials containing a binder. Fr. pat. 1,481,855(April 10, 1967); ABIPC 40:A1709.

This pat. on flameproofing cellulosic matls. with bromides and oxybromides, is similar to Brit. pat. 1,080,845 (see Abstr. No. 96) and Can. pat. 796,224 (see Abstr. No. 120).

99. Israel, Government of. Process for flameproofing lignocellulosic materials. Fr. pat. 1,482,791(April 17, 1967); ABIPC 40:A1747.

This pat. on flameproofing LC matls. such as wood pulps, by impregnation with a halide or a halogen, is similar to Brit. pat. 1,101,249 (see Abstr. No. 97).

100. Israeli Institute for Fibres & Forestry Products. Process proofs wood and fiberboard against fire. Pkg. News 12, no. 2:28(Feb., 1965); ABIPC 35:A8036.

Wood, hardboard, plywood, solid-fiber and corrugated pbd., jute, and sisal can be trd. to prevent ignition even in a furnace and to be self-extinguishing by a new bromination process which does not affect the strength props. and color of the LC matls. Pulps are suspended in a room-temp. soln. of I and K or Mg bromide, then gaseous Cl is introduced to form bromo-chloride which brominates the lignin. Amts. of Br used for substitution equal ca. 2-3% active Cl, and the reaction is conducted so as to exhaust and completely utilize the Br in the bath. The reaction can be carried out in conventional pulp-mill chlorination towers.

101. John, R. Trend in the wood-particle board production and utilization in Czechoslovakia and abroad. Drevo 26, no. 4:117-20(April, 1971); Czech.; ABIPC 42:A5846.

Individual parameters, i.e., thickness, surface quality, swelling characs., strength, and flameproofness of wood-particle board mfd. in Czechoslovakia are discussed and the neg. effect of the poor quality on particle board utilization in the past is noted. The high flexibility of foreign wood particle board mfrs., i.e., their ability to prod. board in size and quality required by the customer is pointed out. The possible use of particle board in agricultural utility construction, roof covering, etc., is discussed.

102.   Johnson, R. E. Plant experiences and problems with fire retardants [for particle boards]. Proc. Symp. Particleboard (Wash. State Univ.) 2:123-7 (March, 1968); ABIPC 42:A2576.

Flakeboard is mfd. at the Arcata, Calif., plant of Humboldt Flakeboard by the Behr process from planer shavings. The flameproofing chemical (''polybor'') is applied in aq. soln. to the green flake processing stage, and ammonium sulfate is added to the water at the resin system. The combination requires a slightly longer press cycle than does untrd. board, and the trd. board is more expensive, but finds a special market mainly as core stock for veneer overlays.

103.   Kaila, A. A. Method of treatment of a porous substance, especially treatment of semisolid wallboard with fire- and other extinguishing substances. U.S. pat. 3,516,851(June 23, 1970); ABIPC 41:A3841.

The method for trg. wallboard described in this invention is similar to that described previously in Brit. pat. 1,174,713; see Abstr. No. 89.

104.   Karlholms AB. Improvements in or relating to fire-resistant fiber board. Brit. pat. 1,064,091(April 5, 1967); ABIPC 38:A6435.

A method of making a fire-resistant fiberboard comprises prepg. a wet layer of wood fibers, applg. a suspension of mineral fibers upon the wood fiber layer to form a layer of mineral fibers, and dewatering the composite wet mat through the wood fiber layer. The thicknesses in the final board of the mineral fiber layer and the wood fiber layer are at least 2.5 mm. and 6 mm., resp.

105.   Kasymbekov, S. K. Flameproofing composition. USSR pat. 222,659 (Filed Nov. 19, 1966); Izobret. no. 23:78(1968); ABIPC 39:A6230.

A flameproofing cpn. for wood-particle boards contains 40-45% water glass, 40-45% UF resin, and 10-20% NaCl.

106.   Kawam, A. Fireproof building structure. Can. pat. 837,567(March 24, 1970); ABIPC 41:A3843.

A fire-resistant particle board is formed of a mixt. of wood particles and unexpanded vermiculite or perlite ore, together with a suitable synt. resin binder.

107.   Kawam, A. Wood-particle board containing vermiculite and method of making same. U.S. pat. 3,459,629(Aug. 5, 1969); ABIPC 40:A5356.

A fire-resistant structural board is formed from wood chips and unexpanded vermiculite bonded with a suitable binder. The board can be surfaced on at least one side with a layer of compressed exfoliated vermiculite.

108. Kent, O. S. Some aspects of flame retardant treatments for board. Board 7, no. 11:245, 247(Nov., 1964); ABIPC 35:A8042.

The durability and maintenance aspects (e.g., washing) of building board flame retardant trmts., i.e., deposition of flame-retardant matls. by impregnation, painting with intumescent paint, and surface glazing with silicate-base paint, are briefly revd. Of the 3 trmts., glazing with silicate-based paints is the most durable, esp. to washing. The durabilities of the impregnation and intumescent paint trmts. are dep. on the effect of leaching.

109. Korneev, V. A. Constructional material from logging wastes. Lesnoi Zh. 11, no. 1:105-7(1968); Russ.; ABIPC 39:A2005.

The matl. described is called ''wood concrete'' and is made from logging waste milled to a max. particle size of 50 x 4 mm. To obtain 1 cu.m. wood concrete, 250 kg. of wood particles are mixed with 220 kg. portland cement, 3 kg. water glass or Ca chloride, and 460 kg. water. The operations can be easily mechanized, and the cost of the prod. is much lower than that of bricks or wood. The new matl. is suitable for the construction of walls, and its water resistance and insulation props. can be brought to the std. level by applg. a protective coating contg. cement, sand, a lacquer, a white pigment (ZnO), and, if desired, pigments of various colors. The wood concrete has a compression strength of 20-30 kg./sq.cm., a bending strength (upon stretch) of 7-11 kg./sq.cm., a d. of 500-700 kg./cu.m., and a heat conductivity coeff. of 0.11-0.12. It is flame resistant, resistant to biol. degradation, and when coated, has a WV permeability coeff. of 0.0039. In 1965, the wood concrete was used for the construction of an exptl. house in Arkhangel'sk to det. its resistance to the climate of the northern zone. The performance of the house has been satisfactory.

110. Kuhr, J.; Weinbach, H. Flame-resistant wood-chip panels containing fully hardened urea-formaldehyde as flame retardant. U.S. pat. 3,535,199(Oct. 20, 1970); ABIPC 41:A7939.

A flame-resistant wood-particle board consists of wood chips, an adhesive such as PF or UF resin, and a powderlike fully hardened UF resin. The last-named component is preformed before addn. to the board-forming cpn., and may be included in the surface layers (or in one surface layer) only.

111. Kuhr, J.; Weinbach, H. Flame-retarding wood chipboard. Brit. pat. 1,228,954(April 21, 1971); CA 75:A22898.

Fire-resistant chipboards were made from chips mixed with 5-25% powdered hardened urea-HCHO resin (I) (100 micrometers or less aminoplast grains), preferably throughout 2 covers and a center layer, and conventionally bonded. Thus, a (I) was mixed with a hardener contg. urea, hexamethylenetetramine, ammonium chloride and water, then heat hardened and used as a 10:90 resin-wood chips mixt. in cover (center) layers contg. 10% (8%) phenolic resin and 0.5% (0.5%) paraffin emulsion.

112. Kurz, F. W. A. Bonding or impregnating composition. Brit. pat. 1,153,299(May 29, 1969); ABIPC 40:A5357.

A cpn. for impregnating building board or the like to impart resistance to moisture, acids, and flame comprises aq. Na or K silicate and 1-34% (based on the silicate wt.) of an oxidic metal cpd. having a particle size below 100 micrometers which precipitates Si dioxide from the silicate to form silica gel. The metal cpd. particles have a smooth sintered surface. The metal cpd. can be an oxide or oxyacid salt of Al, Mg, Pb, Ti, Cr, Fe, Zn, Ba, or Ca.

113. Langguth, R. P.; Vandersall, H. L. Method for fireproofing cellulosic material. U.S. pat. 3,398,019(Aug. 20, 1968); ABIPC 39:A7197.

This invention relates to the flameproofing of wood fiber insulation boards with ammonium salts such as ammonium phosphates which tend to discolor the board during the initial drying of the board. According to the invention, the discoloration is inhibited by incl. in the board (prior to drying and in addn. to the flameproofing agent) either an ammonium carbonate, chloride, fluoride, or sulfide.

114. Lard, E. W.; White, A. C. Noncombustible paperlike sheets. Fr. Demande 2,026,511(Oct. 23, 1970); CA 75:A6949.

A paperlike sheet that does not burn in O is esp. useful as pasteboard, accepts writing or printing, and has good wet strength is prepd. by dispersing 10-80 parts Li, K, Ba, or Be vermiculite in an aq. suspension contg. 5-40 parts asbestos, 5-60 parts glass fibers, 2-10 parts synt. polymer latex binder, and 0.01-1% flocculating agent, such as a mixt. of 4 ml. concd. sulfuric acid, 2.9 g. Ca acid phosphate hydrate, 0.4 g. Mg chloride sexahydrate, and 0.2 g. LiCl in 7.6 l. water, forming a sheet of the fibrous cpn., and drying the sheet.

115. Lee, T. G.; Loftus, J. J.; Gross, D. Effect of moisture on surface flammability of coated and uncoated cellulosic materials. ASTM Special Tech. Publ. no. 385 (''Moisture in materials in relation to fire test''):112-23(June 24, 1964; publ. 1965); ABIPC 36:A5584.

A method is described for rapid in situ detn. of the ''thermal inertia for surface heating'' (I) of matls., using a sensitive IR detector. Exptl. measurements are given of the effect of moisture content on (I) and on the surface flammability of selected cellulosic matls. (hardboards and painted and unpainted fiberboards) conditioned to equil. at RH values from 0 to 99%. The (I) of uncoated hardboards and fiberboards can be represented as a linear function of their moisture content. If the appropriate thermal props. are taken into account, the flame-spread factor is inversely proportional to (I). The unbroken surface film of coated matls. results in a lower ignition sensitivity than that predicted on the basis of (I) values.

116. Leonovich, A. A. Properties of fireproofed hardboards. Sb. Tr. Vses. Nauch.-Issled., Eksp.-Konstr. Inst. Tary Upakovki no. 5:172-7(1969); ABIPC 42:A6916.

Hardboards mfd. according to USSR pat. 195,626 (cf. ABIPC 38:A4917), were tested to det. their suitability for use as a pkg. matl. for export and for special goods. Since the tempering time determines the important props. of the hardboards, both tempered and nontempered samples were tested. Tempering

had little effect on the mech. strength of the boards, but the necessity of
carrying it out was shown by the behavior of the samples exposed to the action
of water. Nontempered boards sorbed more moisture and at equal amts. of
sorbed moisture, swelled more than tempered boards. Tempering also converted
the flameproofing cpn. (phosphoric acid, urea, and dicyandiamide) into an insol.
form, preventing its leaching upon prolonged immersion in water. Incorporation
into the boards of 3% PF resin decreased the 24-hr. water absorption. Immersion
in water for up to 20 days had little effect on the mech. strength of tempered
boards, but significantly reduced that of nontempered samples. Chem. anal. showed
that the boards release ammonia and amines, but the amts. released did not exceed
the max. permissible concn. for residential dwellings: the amts. were 19 mg.
ammonia and 0.9 mg. amines (as diethylamine)/cu.m. during the first 12 hr.

117. Leonovich, A. A.; Koromyslova, L. V.; Shishkina, N. N. Flame resistant
wood fiberboards. Nauch. Tr. Leningr. Lesotekh. Akad. no. 100:341-2(1967); Russ.;
ABIPC 39:A4819.

Fiberboards, mfd. by the air-deposition process, are made flame resistant
without significant loss of mech. strength by trmt. with an aq. soln. of orthophosphoric acid neutd. to pH 5 with urea or dicyandiamide. The min. amt. of
phosphate needed for effective flameproofing is 3% P. The boards retain their
flame resistance after prolonged soaking in water.

118. Leonovich, A. A.; Solechnik, N. Y. Manufacturing technology and
properties of flameproof wood fiberboards. Holztechnol. 10, no. 4:219-24(Nov.,
1969); Ger.; ABIPC 41:A399.

Data are presented on the flameproof props. of fiberboards which have been
trd. using a newly devd. dry flameproofing process involving spraying of the
fiberboard raw matl. with an agent incorporating orthophosphoric acid and N-
contg. org. bases. The flameproof props. are shown to result from a lowering
of the threshold temp. of active pyrolysis and redn. in the amt. of volatile
substances formed during pyrolysis. Special problems involved in the mfr. of
such flameproofed fiberboards are also examd. The presence of the flameproofing
agent alters the required pressing conditions (reduced temp. and pressure). Also,
there is an optimum length of hardening with respect to board strength props. The
boards can be used in applns. where they are subjected to changing climatic
conditions and vibrations.

119. Leonovich, A. A.; Solechnik, N. Y.; Brovkina, V. I. Method for the
production of hardboards. USSR pat. 268,639; publ. Otkryt. Izobret. 47, no.
14:69(April 10, 1970); ABIPC 41:A5923.

Hardboards produced by the wet method are made fireproof and of better
quality by soaking the finished boards in a 10-35% aq. soln. of orthophosphoric
acid neutd. with organic bases, at 50-85 C. for 3-40 sec., fld. by pressing and
drying to a moisture content of 2-8%, dry pressing at a pressure of 20-30 kg./
sq.cm., and tempering.

120. Lewin, M. Fire-proofing of bonded cellulosic and lignocellulosic
articles. Can. pat. 796,224(Oct., 8, 1968); ABIPC 39:A6837.

This process for flameproofing cellulosic articles (incl. paper and pbd., particle board, etc.) is similar to that described in Brit. pat. 1,080,845; see Abstr. No. 96.

121. Lewin, M. Fire-proofing of cellulosic material with a bonding agent containing bromides. U.S. pat. 3,484,340(Dec. 16, 1969); ABIPC 40:A8122.

This process for fireproofing cellulosic matls. such as paper and particle board is similar to that described previously in Brit. pat. 1,080,845; see Abstr. No. 96.

122. Lewin, M. Flameproofing of lignocellulosic material. Can. pat. 834,719(Feb. 17, 1970); ABIPC 41:A893.

The process for flameproofing of LC matl. described in this pat. is similar to that described previously in Brit. pat. 1,101,249; see Abstr. No. 97.

123. Lundgren, S. A. Improving the fire resistance of fiberboard. Swed. pat. 194,193(Feb. 2, 1965); ABIPC 36:A8474.

The fire resistance of fiberboard is increased by trmt. with superheated steam at about 200 C. for a sufficiently long time to liberate all components of the board that are volatile at this temp.

124. Lurie, D. Process for the manufacture of a flameproofing agent, agent thus obtained, and use of the agent in flameproofed articles such as flameproofed panels. Fr. pat. 1,529,506(May 13, 1968); ABIPC 40:A6998.

A combination flameproofing/binding agent for particle board or the like consists of a powder or suspension contg. a substance, such as starch or a starch deriv., causing swelling under the action of heat; a mineral or org. polymer, such as PVAc or a UF resin; a thermal expansion agent, such as oxalic acid; and an auxiliary flameproofing agent, such as ammonium phosphate.

125. M & T Chemicals Inc. Improvements in and relating to flame-resistant boards. Brit. pat. 1,055,759(Jan. 18, 1967); ABIPC 38:A2382.

A process for making a flame-resistant wood-particle board comprises coating the wood particles with a thermally unstable Cl cpd. (e.g., chlorinated paraffin wax) and an Sb cpd. such as Sb trioxide or pentoxide, separately coating the particles with adhesive, forming the particles into a mat, and pressing and curing the mat.

126. Makinen, A. Surface impregnation of building boards: results of some practical experiments. Paperi Puu 50, no. 11:669-71, 673-5(Nov., 1968); Swed.; ABIPC 40:A336.

Plywood, particle board, hardboard, sawn timber, and paper were surface impregnated with a mixt. of unsatd. polyester and styrene monomers by low-pressure trmt. for a few seconds, fld. by polymn. in a hot-press within 1-5 min., and removal of excess plastic by doctoring (shaving). All board prods. yielded a smooth surface corresp. in quality to that of the press platens. By

surface trg. decorative paper and polymg. it in a hot-press simult. with the
base board, one can obtain decorative patterned prods. at lower prodn. costs
than for traditional melamine-phenol laminates. Although the polyester-styrene
mixt. did not impart a weatherproof surface, the process can be combined with
simult. lamination to achieve weather, flame, and/or fungus resistance. The
process lends itself to the mfr. of different profiles and prods., such as
parquet flooring. Several kinds of plastics can be used for impregnation, their
amt. varying from 300 to 600 g./sq.m. of board surface. The plastic consumption
can be regulated by controlling the underpressure and viscy. and by addn. of
fillers. A prototype model of an ind.-scale rapid impregnating app. was
constructed and tried out. On sawn goods it gave satisfactory results, e.g.,
by bringing out the natural grain of wood. Redwood gained a slight reddish
tone, but resin flow should also be considered.

127. Makinen, A. E. Improvements in or relating to the treatment of
porous bodies. Brit. pat. 1,220,525(Jan. 27, 1971); ABIPC 42:A6464.

The process for trg. particle board or the like described in this
invention is similar to that described previously in Can. pat. 859,087; see
flg. abstr.

128. Makinen, A. E. Method for the impregnation and surface treatment
of porous board type products. Can. pat. 859,087(Dec. 22, 1970); ABIPC 41:A10985.

A method for impregnating and surface trg. porous board prods. (e.g.,
particle board, wallboard, etc.), so as to improve certain props. (e.g., strength,
fire resistance, etc., according to the trmt. agent used) comprises introducing
the board prods. into a vacuum chamber where they are retained, immersed in a
trg. medium, for not more than 5 min., adjusting the pressure in the chamber
to atm., retaining the boards in the trg. medium for an addnl. period of time
not to exceed 5 min., and removing the boards from the chamber.

129. Maku, T.; Sasaki, H.; Ishihara, S.; Kimoto, K.; Kamo, H. On some
properties of composite panels. Wood Res. (Kyoto) no. 44:21-52(July, 1968);
Jap.; ABIPC 40:A1139.

Composite building panels were evald. for thermal conductivity, warping
as a function of moisture content, bending strength, elastic modulus, and
esp. flame resistance. Matls. used as laminate plies included decorative white
lauan sliced veneer, lauan plywood, wood fiber insulation board, particle board,
bagasse particle board, paper honeycomb, PS foam, flameproofed lauan plywood and
particle board (trd. with fire retardants), cement-excelsior board, gypsum
board, Al plate, perlite board, and asbestos-cement board. Results are shown
in tables and graphs.

130. Maxwell, J. W. Automatic handling of chemicals in particle board
plants. Proc. Symp. Particleboard (Wash. State Univ.) 3:73-89(March, 1969);
ABIPC 42:A2591.

Particle board factories handle 3-30 million lb. of chem. additives yearly,
of which ca. 80% are UF resins; the rest include PF resins, wax emulsions,
catalysts (ammonium chloride or sulfate), termite repellents, and flame retardants.
Bulk handling, shipment, storage, and dosage (mixing) of these chemicals are
discussed, with emphasis on autom. methods.

131. Morze, Z.; Nowak, K.; Peretiatkowicz, E. Flameproofing of particle boards. Rocz. Wyzsz. Szkoly Roln. Poznan 39:113-23(1968); Pol.; CA 72:A102020.

The addn. of 10% Pyrmolit (I) (mineral origin and contg. Ca carbonate) to beechwood particle board increased the flame resistance. The phys. props. of the particle boards were not changed when (I) was added to the urea adhesive-wood mixt. together with a dry adhesive contg. ammonium sulfate as hardener. These boards decreased 9.29% by wt. during 10 min. heating in an open flame supplying 50 kcal./min. After removal of the flame, the boards ceased to smoulder in 2-3 min.

132. National Gypsum Co. Self-extinguishing wood fiberboard. Brit. pat. 1,242,697(Aug. 11, 1971); CA 75:A142117.

A fire-resistant fiberboard was prepd. by incorporating into the fiber 30-50 wt. % Mg hydroxide, which gave off water at high temp. For example, a fiberboard prepd. from pinewood fiber 460, Mg hydroxide 150, tapioca starch 9, rosin 2.5, and wax 1.25 lb. with a trace of alum to control pH formed 1000 sq.ft. of 1/2 in. thick fiberboard, which passed the Class I fire rating.

133. Nielsen, C. L. Process for preparing fire-retardant bituminous shingles by coating same with thermosetting acrylic resin. U.S. pat. 3,276,906 (Oct. 4, 1966); ABIPC 37:A7894.

A process for making a flame-retardant roofing matl. comprises applg. a coating of an aq. soln. of a thermosetting acrylic resin to a fiber felt satd. with asphalt or tar, then evapg. the solvent.

134. Nystroem, E. H. B. Fire-resistant board material. Can. pat. 753,152 (Feb. 21, 1967); ABIPC 38:A3220.

This board is similar to that described in Fr. pat. 1,349,973; see Abstr. No. 136.

135. Nystroem, E. H. B. Fire-resistant board material. Can. pat. 786,233 (May 28, 1968); ABIPC 39:A4415.

This fire-resistant fiber building board is similar to that described in Brit. pat. 1,019,208; see Abstr. No. 138.

136. Nystroem, E. H. B. Flame resistant board made of mineral fibers. Fr. pat. 1,349,973(Dec. 16, 1963); ABIPC 36:A6079.

This pat. is similar to Brit. pat. 958,468; see Abstr. No. 139.

137. Nystroem, E. H. B. Improved fire-resistant board material. Brit. pat. 1,070,737(June 1, 1967); ABIPC 38:A7257.

A fire-resistant building board consists of a water-laid felt of mineral fibers bound together by an org. binder (e.g., starch) and reinforced by incorporation of metal, plastic, or glass prods., such as wire netting.

138. Nystroem, E. H. B. Improvements in and relating to fire-resistant board material. Brit. pat. 1,019,208(Feb. 2, 1966); ABIPC 37:A5526.

In the mfr. of a fire-resistant board consisting of water-laid mineral
fibers bound with an org. binder, in which drying of the board is effected in
a hot press, the d. of the finished board is caused to vary across the thickness
of the board by varying the pressure appl. during the drying period.

139. Nystroem, E. H. B. Improvements in or relating to fire-resistant
board material. Brit. pat. 958,468(May 21, 1964); ABIPC 35:A5114.

A fire-resistant board consists of water-laid felted mineral fibers bonded
with an org. binder (e.g., starch), the board having a d. of 0.5-1.1 g./cc.,
with the fibers in the board being in a condition of elastic compression. This
condition of the fibers is brought about by using a rel. low pressure during
the pressing of the boards, so that the fibers are not crushed.

140. Nystroem, E. H. B. Method for production of a fire-resistant mineral
fiberboard with starch binder. U.S. pat. 3,376,189(April 2, 1968); ABIPC 39:A2554.

The process comprises mixing synt. mineral fibers, water, and ungelatinized
starch; adjusting the pH of the mixt. to 4.2-6.9; forming the mixt. into a wet
mat; cutting the mat into sheets; subjecting test sheets to pressure tests to
det. in which range of pressure fiber crushing takes place; and applg. to the
sheets a pressure below this range for 10-120 min. at 140-220 C. so as to dry
the sheets and gelatinize the starch. The pressure should be sufficient to
produce a board having a d. of 0.5-1.1 g./cu.cm.

141. Orth, G. O., Jr.; Pevey, C. V.; Reichman, E. J. Lignocellulosic
product. Can. pat. 786,755(June 4, 1968); ABIPC 39:A4416.

This prod. (a hardboard or the like building board which is resistant to
flame and water) is similar to that described in U.S. pat. 3,245,870; see flg.
abstr.

142. Orth, G. O., Jr.; Pevey, C. V.; Reichman, E. J. Process of producing a
water-resistant and fire-retardant lignocellulosic product. U.S. pat. 3,245,870
(April 12, 1966); ABIPC 37:A2432.

A process for prodg. a water-resistant and fire-retardant insulation board
or the like comprises wetting LC fibers (e.g., wood fibers or the like) with a
soln. contg. rosin size and a pptg. agent such as alum, adjusting the pH to an
acidic condition with buffered boric acid while pptg. the size on the fibers,
and drying while using the buffered boric acid to keep the pH low enough so as
to maintain the pptn. of the size.

143. Otlivanchik, A. N.; Ioffe, A. L.; Dmitrieva, G. A. Flameproofing of
fiberboards. Derevoobrabat. Prom. 15, no. 1:8-10(Jan., 1966); Russ.; SLA transl.
in Engl. (5 p.) available from IPC at copying cost; ABIPC 37:A2012; 38:A9244.

The protective efficiency of flameproofing cpns. and paints (incl. cpns.
based on furfural-acetone and UF resins, on chlorinated org. cpds., and silicate-
base paints) were tested on samples of domestic hardboards and insulating boards
from several mfg. plants. The results of the tests (degree of flame resistance,
of biol. resistance, and phys.-mech. props. of the boards) are tabulated. All

cpns. gave satisfactory protection of the samples. Recommendations are made on
the appln. methods to be used, the amts. of the cpds./sq.m. board, etc. The
flameproofing should be carried out at ambient temp., but not below 10 C.,
preferably in two trmts. with drying between them. Depending on the nature of
the cpns., the amts. to be used per sq.m. range from 650 to 1400 g. The trd.
boards, which have also a satisfactory resistance against the action of micro-
organisms, can be used in construction for outside paneling.

144. Paper Trade Journal. Paperboard housing offers low-cost shelter with
20-year life. Paper Trade J. 154, no. 4:71-2(Jan. 26, 1970); ABIPC 40:A385.

A method of prodg. low-cost pbd. housing has been devd. by Universal
Papertech Corp. (Hatfield, Pa.). The basic matl. is a special corrugated
board chemically impregnated to resist water, fire, and vermin. The board is
further strengthened on the construction site with Fiberglas and polyester
resins. The basic housing unit is 20 x 21.5 ft. at the base, has an 8 ft.
ceiling, and costs about $800.00. These units may be linked in different ways
so as to meet a variety of needs.

145. Pataki, A. A.; Hossain, S. U.; Johnson, W. P. Flame-retardant particle
board. Can. pat. 713,000(July 6, 1965); ABIPC 36:A4528.

A flame-retardant wood particle board is formed by pretrg. the particles
with a soln. of a borate and an inorg. acid, such as Na tetraborate and HCl.

146. Pataki, A. A.; Hossain, S. U.; Johnson, W. P. Flame-retardant particle
board containing acidified borate and process for making the same. U.S. pat.
3,321,421(May 23, 1967); ABIPC 38:A4095.

A process for making flame-retardant particle board from wood flakes involves
the step of applg. to the flakes a soln. consisting of an aq. soln. of a borate
such as Na tetraborate acidified with an inorg. acid such as HCl.

147. Price, F. W.; Koopmann, H. F. Fire-resistant asphalt roofing and
method of manufacture. U.S. pat. 3,193,439(July 6, 1965); ABIPC 36:A4531.

A fire-resistant asphalt roofing matl. comprises a conventional asphalt-
satd. felt base coated with another asphalt cpn. having a higher softening point
than that of the satg. asphalt, with the asphalt coating incl. a layer of glass
fibers. The asphalt used for coating is a type which forms a scum when subjected
to fire.

148. Prosinski, S.; Lutomski, K.; Piotrewicz, Z. Flameproofing of cork
insulating panels. Roc. Wyzsz. Szk. Roln. Poznaniu 39:201-20(1968); Pol.; CA
72:A80396.

Cork panels were impregnated with 30% diammonium phosphate (I) soln., 30%
aq. 1:1 (I)-ammonium sulfate (II) mixt., or 25% Silignit RM (III) (com. mixt.
of (I), (II), surfactant, and fungicide) soln. Some test panels were also flameproofed by painting with a 70% aq. suspension of Pyrochron S-4 (IV) (HCHO-urea
resin, monoammonium phosphate, and fungicide mixt.), or Ignisol Dx (V) (oil-
base paint contg. ZnO, lithopone, white Pb, linseed oil, turpentine, and drier).

The most effective flameproofing was obtained by impregnating the panels for 1 hr. in 25% (III) soln.; (I) or (I)-(III) mixt. penetrated only to a depth of 10 mm. and did not protect thicker panels. The flameproofing with (V) required 2 kg. (V)/sq.m.; (IV) was not effective.

149. Quigg, P. S.; Nelsson, N. Structural member with multilayered gypsum board fire protection. U.S. pat. 3,217,456(Nov. 16, 1965); ABIPC 36:A8477.

Several layers of paper-faced gypsum board are secured with wire binding elts. and joint cpd. about a structural member such as a steel girder to form a fire-resistant assembly.

150. Quinn, R. G. Building material laminate. U.S. pat. 3,427,216(Feb. 11, 1969); ABIPC 40:A844.

A structural sheet matl. having good weathering and fire resistant props. comprises a cellulosic board such as plywood laminated with a fire-resistant adhesive to a surface layer of asbestos paper contg. a water-insol. binder (which will not support combustion) to increase wet strength. PVC is a suitable binder.

151. Quinn, R. G. Building material laminate. Can. pat. 808,149(March 11, 1969); ABIPC 40:A3537.

A laminate of use as a building board and having improved resistance to fire and weathering consists of a base such as plywood laminated to a layer of asbestos paper contg. a water-insol. binder to increase its wet strength. PVC is a suitable binder.

152. Rannila, T. V. Fireproof fiberboard. Finn. pat. 33,060(Aug. 31, 1963); ABIPC 35:A5116.

Fire resistance is achieved by adding equiv. amts. of ferrous ammonium sulfate and KAl sulfate to the portland cement binder.

153. Roberts, J. R. Fire-resistant porous acoustic board with perforations through metal facing sheet. U.S. pat. 3,498,404(March 3, 1970); ABIPC 41:A878.

This acoustical ceiling board consists of a porous backing (the usual ceiling board matl., such as a sheet formed of paper pulp, mineral wool, and starch) to which is adhered a metal facing sheet by means of an acrylic adhesive. Perforations are formed in the metal facing sheet, and these perforations are extended through a portion of the thickness of the backing board.

154. Sammon Rulla Oy. Treatment of the surface of porous fiberboard impregnated with a fireproofing agent. Finn. pat. 34,854(Jan. 15, 1966); ABIPC 37:A862.

A paper surfacing layer is laminated to fiberboard using as adhesive a water-sol. amino resin or a PVC emulsion contg. flameproofing agents (e.g., urea phosphate) in the aq. phase.

155. Savkovic, S. Improvements in or relating to fireproofing. Brit. pat. 1,167,706(Oct. 22, 1969); ABIPC 40:A10287.

A process for prepg. a soln. for fireproofing matls. such as wood, textiles, pbd., and the like comprises filtering the prod. obtained by heating and mixing the flg.: water, K alum, boric acid, borax, Mg sulfate, ammonium sulfate, and ammonium carbonate.

156. Schmidt-Hellerau, C. Use of modified melamine-urea formaldehyde resins for the preparation of highly weather-resistant particle boards. Holz-Zentralbl. no. 145:2227-8(Dec. 3, 1969); Original in Ger. not available; transl. in Engl. (14 p.) available from IPC at copying cost; ABIPC 42:A434.

Studies show that particle boards incorporating MF or MF-UF binders possess weathering resistances considerably below those of boards incorporating PF binders. However, by including a special curing stage flg. pressing and using a 33% higher binder content, the resistance of the MF-UF-resin board can be brought almost on a par with that of PF-resin board. The advantages of the former include reduced water absorption, shorter pressing times, cheaper fungicidal protection, simpler flame-resistance finishing, improved lacquer adhesion, and a lighter board color.

157. Schoenenberger, K. B. Method of producing pressed chip bodies of low inflammability. Can. pat. 788,900(July 2, 1968); ABIPC 39:A5335.

This process for making fire-resistant boards and the like from wood chips or similar matls. is similar to that described in Brit. pat. 1,089,836; see Abstr. No. 78.

158. Schroeder, J. F. Fire-resistant asphalt roofing. Can. pat. 846,763 (July 14, 1970); ABIPC 41:A7945.

A fire-resistant asphalt roof covering matl. comprises a mineral wool felt base coated with a cpn. incl. asphalt, ground trap rock filler, and asbestos. The felt base may include a portion of cellulose fibers, and is impregnated with asphalt.

159. Schuetz, C. C.; Ericson, R. Fire-resistant building covering composition. U.S. pat. 3,369,956(Feb. 20, 1968); ABIPC 39:A1643.

This roofing matl. consists of a base (an asphalt-impregnated felt), a layer of asphalt on the base, a glass fiber mat embedded in the coating, and mineral granules embedded in the surface of the asphalt layer.

160. Schuetz, C. C.; Ericson, R. Fire-resistant building covering composition. Can. pat. 755,591(March 28, 1967); ABIPC 38:A4916.

This fire-resistant roofing matl. consists of a base of roofing felt, an asphalt layer on the base, an open integral mat of glass fibers of uniform diam. embedded in the asphalt layer, and roofing granules partially embedded in the upper surface of the asphalt.

161. Shannon, R. F. Fibrous acoustical panel with impregnant in rear body portion. U.S. pat. 3,333,656(Aug. 1, 1967); ABIPC 38:A6439.

An acoustical panel formed of bonded mineral fibers is impregnated from
the rear, through a portion of the panel thickness, with a stiffening and fire-
resistant cpn. such as K silicate.

162. Shannon, R. F. Fire-resistant glass fiberboard and method of making
same. U.S. pat. 3,470,977(Oct. 7, 1969); ABIPC 40:A6349.

A method of prodg. a fire-resistant acoustical panel comprises depositing
swirls of glass fibers onto a surface, applg. a devitrifying agent and a curable
binder to the fibers, curing the binder, and forming a multitude of short slits
in the front face of the panel.

163. Shisko, W. S. Fire-resistant board. Can. pat. 821,990(Sept. 2, 1969);
ABIPC 40:A9560.

A fire-resistant acoustical board is formed from a furnish incl. mineral
wool, asbestos fibers, clay, and unexpanded vermiculite. When subjected to
heat, the vermiculite expands so as to increase the thickness of the board and
therefore its resistance to heat conduction.

164. Shisko, W. S. Incombustible board containing mineral and cellulosic
fibers and metal oxide and method therefor. U.S. pat. 3,220,918(Nov. 30, 1965);
ABIPC 36:A8422.

A method of making an incombustible board comprises forming a slurry of
cellulosic and mineral fibers incl. 25-75% of the cellulosic fibers, adding to
the slurry an oxide of Mg, Ca, or Zn in an amt. of 40-200% of the wt. of the
fibers, adding a sulfate such as alum in an amt. of 10-200% of the fiber wt.,
and forming the slurry into board.

165. Smith, F. C.; Thornton, J. Treatment of insulation board. Brit.
pat. 994,988(June 10, 1965); ABIPC 36:A6862.

In the mfr. of insulation board, the fire-retardant props. of the board
are improved by drawing a soln. of a fire-retardant cpd. into and at least
partially through the board by the controlled appln. of different pressures
on the opposite sides of the board. The trmt. is carried out after the board
has been formed and dewatered, but before it has been dried. The fire
retardant can be an alkali metal or ammonium borate or phosphate.

166. Societe Anonyme Francaise du Ferodo. Covering material and process
for its manufacture. Fr. pat. 1,582,087(Aug. 18, 1969); ABIPC 41:A4621.

A fireproof roofing matl. consists of compressed asbestos-fiber pbd.
mfd. using a 10% bitumen-emulsion binder in the stock.

167. Solechnik, N. Y.; Leonovich, A. A. Method of making hardboards. USSR
pat. 195,626(Filed March 26, 1966); Publ. Izobret. no. 10:67(1967); ABIPC 38:A4917.

Flame-resistant hardboards are obtained by using as binder additive, a soln.
neutd. to pH 5, contg., per 100 wt. parts of o.d. wood fibers, 7-12 parts orthophosphoric acid, 15-21 parts urea, and 9-19 parts dicyandiamide. The cpn. is
incorporated during the mixing of wood with the binder, then the mixt. is dried
to 5-6% moisture content, and pressed under 25-30 kg./sq.cm. at 180-200 C.

168.   Solechnik, N. Y.; Leonovich, A. A.; Barashkova, L. I.   Effect of the components of a flameproofing composition on the properties of constructional fiberboards.   Lesnoi Zh. 11, no. 6:116-20(1968); Russ.; ABIPC 39:A9657.

The flameproofing cpn. for building boards mfd. by the dry process contains phosphoric acid, urea, and dicyandiamide.   The degree of flame resistance is detd. primarily by the content of the acid; the two bases reduce the degrading effect of the acid and thus prevent excessive redn. of the board mech. strength. Factorial anal. was used to det. the effects of individual components of the mixt. Each of the 3 components was incorporated into the cpn. at two levels, so that 8 different cpns. were obtained and used for impregnation of pinewood defibrator pulp.   The impregnated pulp samples were then formed into boards by air deposition, molding at 180 C., and curing at 160 C.   The amts. of phosphoric acid were 2.5 and 3%, based on fiber wt., those of urea 2 and 3 mole/mole acid, and those of dicyandiamide 1 and 2 mole/mole acid.   The amts. of acid used have been shown to give satisfactory flame resistance.   An increase of the acid content reduces the mech. strength and increases the water absorption of the boards.   Urea reduces the action of the acid on fibers, but increases the water absorption. Dicyandiamide, in combination with urea, improves both the mech. strength and water absorption, and does not decompose during curing.

169.   Stiftelsen Wallboardindustriens Forskningsinstitut.   Fire-resistant, wood-based boards.   Brit. pat. 1,242,290(Aug. 11, 1971); CA 75:A130978.

Fire-resistant wood boards were prepd. comprising a granular fire-retardant, e.g., diammonium hydrogen phosphate (I), borax, boric acid, and (or) urea, and an inert water-resistant coating.   Wood pulp was mixed with 20% granular 10:20:20 N-P-K fertilizer, composed of (I) and KCl, and with gypsum and stearic acid derivs., converted to sheets, pressed, dried, and conditioned to give a fire resistant board.   The boards may be sprayed before pressing with aq. boric acid, borax, and urea soln. to improve their fire resistance.

170.   Sukhanov, V. S.; Nadubov, V. A.; Kashuba, I. I.; Lubennikov, V. I.; Pedak, V. P.; Brazhnik, D. E.; Tverdokhleb, A. I.; Dremov, A. V.; Malinovskii, M. S.; Bairak, V. I.   Composition for the manufacture of building materials. USSR pat. 272,870.   Publ. Otkryt. Izobret. 47, no. 19:171(June 3, 1970); ABIPC 41:A7947.

A flame-resistant cpn. for the mfr. of constructional matls., incl. a synt. binder, a filler, and an additive, contains (in wt. %):   biuret-formaldehyde resin 5-50; wood flour 50-95; and ammonium salts no less than 20% above 100.

171.   Thaler, H. J.   Process for the manufacture of flame-resistant fibrous material containing cellulose.   Fr. pat. 1,369,817(July 6, 1964); ABIPC 37:A2876.

A process for the mfr. of flame-resistant fibrous matl. contg. cellulose involves adjusting the pH of a fibrous slurry incorporating Na silicate to 8.3-6.8 resulting in the pptn. of silicic acid gel onto the fibers.

172.   Thaler, H. J.   Process for the production of cellulosic fibrous materials of low flammability.   Can. pat. 812,194(May 6, 1969); ABIPC 40:A2278.

This process for redg. the flammability of cellulosic fibrous matls.,
particularly fiberboard, is similar to that described in Fr. pat. 1,369,817;
see preceding abstr.

173. Thaler, H. J. Process for the production of cellulosic fibrous
materials of low inflammability. Brit. pat. 1,051,455(Dec. 14, 1966); ABIPC 38:A1341.

A process for flameproofing cellulose fibers (e.g., in the prodn. of fiberboard) is similar to that described in Fr. pat. 1,369,817; see Abstr. No. 171.

174. Thiery, P. Fireproofing sheet materials. Papeterie 93, no. 5:440,
443-8(1971); Fr.; CA 75:A50577.

The fireproofing of cellulosic sheet building matl., i.e., sheet and
kraft carton matl. and paper laminates, with fireproofing additives was
discussed. 33 ref.

175. Thompson, R.; Arthur, L. T. Fire-retardant composition. Brit. pat.
1,132,715(Nov. 6, 1968); ABIPC 40:A5371.

A cpn. for use in imparting fire-retardant props. to particle board, hardboard, and the like consists of an aq. soln. of an alkali metal or ammonium
borate and a water-insol. fire-retardant agent such as chlorinated wax.

176. Usines, R. & R. Dheedene, SA. Insulating boards from wood wool. Fr.
pat. 1,359,729(March 23, 1964); ABIPC 36:A8482.

Light wt., nonflammable insulating boards are made of a core of foamed
plastic matl. such as PS or PVC, and external layers of mineralized wood fibers,
wood wool, or chips. The wood matl. is impregnated in a cement or magnesia
bath, and the layers of the board are assembled under a slight pressure by
means of a bonding agent.

177. Videen, O. R. Fire-retardant fiberboard with fire-retardant
hydrated borate. Can. pat. 731,049(March 29, 1966); ABIPC 37:A2437.

This fiberboard prod. is similar to that described in U.S. pat. 3,202,570;
see flg. abstr.

178. Videen, O. R. Method of forming a fiberboard containing a fire-
retardant hydrated borate and product thereof. U.S. pat. 3,202,570(Aug. 24,
1965); ABIPC 36:A6088.

A fire-retardant board is formed from a furnish incl., in addn. to the
usual fibers, finely divided particles of colemanite, ulexite, or Gerstley
borate.

179. Voelskow, P. Process for the manufacture of fire-resistant particle
board. Ger. pat. 1,165,248(Sept. 24, 1964); ABIPC 35:A6800.

A process for the mfr. of wood-particle board suitable for use as building
board (particularly with respect to fire resistance, heat insulation, water
resistance, and mech. strength props.) involves mixing the wood chips with an
aq. soln. of monomeric urea and HCHO, a conventional binder (such as urea,

melamine, or phenolic resins), and fire-resisting salts (such as the ammonium salts of strong acids). The process is specifically designed to provide the conditions which will effect impregnation of the wood chips with sufficient amts. of fire-resisting salts without adversely affecting other board props. or the board mfg. process.

180. Walker, R. T.; Schuetz, C. C. Fire-resistant asphalt coating composition and shingle. U.S. pat. 3,180,783(April 27, 1965); ABIPC 36:A2259.

A fire-resistant shingle comprises the usual base felt coated with a cpn. incl. asphalt, glass fibers, unexpanded vermiculite, and conventional fillers. The cpn. is resistant to flow when exposed to flame.

181. Ware, F. Fire-resistant bituminous compositions. U.S. pat. 3,508,934 (April 28, 1970); ABIPC 41:A2841.

Asphalt is blended with inorg. fillers and a particulate naturally-occurring phosphate rock having a particle size of 25-325 mesh and incl. 0.25-40.0% by wt. of phosphorous oxide, and the blend is applied to a satd. felt. The prod. is of use in making roofing and siding elts. of improved fire resistance.

182. Wilhelm, G. F.; Bacon, V. G. Method of forming fire-retardant panels. U.S. pat. 3,480,494(Nov. 25, 1969); ABIPC 40:A8480.

A method of making a fire-resistant panel includes securing a thin layer of cross-banded veneer to an asbestos-fiber core by an adhesive which is allowed to cure, then redg. the thickness of the cross-banded veneer to a thin film, fld. by appln. of an adhesive and a decorative face veneer.

183. Wilhelmi, H.; Neudert, W. Process for treating wood chips with binders and impregnating agents. Ger. pat. 1,224,917(Exam. copy Sept. 15, 1966); ABIPC 39:A772.

A process for the uniform mixing of wood chips with a binder cpn. incorporating various additives (waterproofing and flameproofing agents, etc.), of use in the mfr. of wood-particle board, involves trmt. of the chips in a binder cpn. bath fld. by centrifugation.

184. Zabrodkin, A. G.; Sterlin, D. M.; Khitrova, L. I.; Solomatina, N. S. Manufacture of fire-protective wood chip slabs. USSR pat. 310,819(Aug. 9, 1971); Otkrytiya, Izobret., Prom. Obraztsy, Tovarnye Znaki 48, no. 24:60(1971); CA 76:A26612.

COATINGS

185. Brocklehurst, P. Improvements relating to protective finishes. Brit. pat. 992,458(May 19, 1965); ABIPC 36:A6549.

In the coating or other trmt. of various surfaces with a liquid cpn. contg. a surface-active agent, the residual surface-active agent is removed from the surface after trmt. by employing a tertiary amine oxide as the surface-active agent and then heating the trd. surface at a temp. above 100 C. A typical surface-active agent is N-octadecyl-N,N-dimethylamine oxide. The process is of particular use in trg. cellulosic fabrics with water- and flameproofing cpns. and the like.

186. Compagnie de Saint-Gobain. A new flameproofing and adhesive coating based on alkaline silicate. Fr. pat. 1,322,289(Feb. 18, 1963); ABIPC 35:A4689.

A flameproofing coating agent which does not affect the flexibility of paper contains 1 part of a butadiene-styrene latex (contg. 60% styrene and 40% butadiene) per 4-6 parts of an alk. silicate, such as a com. Na silicate (36 deg. Be) dild. 1:1 with water. The mixt. is dild. to contain 50% solids, and is appl. by any known means to the surface of paper (e.g., kraft wrapping paper) at a rate of 10 g. solids sq.m. The cpn. can be used also, as an adhesive in the mfr. of board, esp. corrugated board, and as a paint by adding appropriate fillers and pigments.

187. Hinds, C. E. Intumescent coated roofing granules and asphalt composition felt-base roofing containing the same. U.S. pat. 3,365,322(Jan. 23, 1968); ABIPC 39:A1632.

A fire-retardant roofing matl. comprises a sheet of a roofing felt impregnated with an asphaltic matl., a lower coating layer of an asphaltic cpn. on one face of the felt, an interlayer of refractory mineral roofing granules adhered to the lower coating layer, an upper coating layer of an asphaltic cpn. over the mineral granules layer, and a layer of decorative mineral granules over the upper asphaltic layer. The granules adhered to the lower coating layer are individually coated with a reaction prod. of Na silicate and borax which intumesces upon exposure of the coated granules to flame temps.

188. Morin, R. L. Flame resistant adhesive. Fr. pat. 1,359,486(March 16, 1964); ABIPC 36:A8209.

The adhesive, suitable for gluing paper (e.g., wallpaper) to flammable surfaces, such as particle board, plywood, and molded wood paneling, and which prevents the spread of fire, contains 52% by wt. of starch or dextrin (or a mixt. of the two), 34% diammonium phosphate, and 14% oxalic acid. The mixt. is dild. with water before use.

189. Peterson, G. J. Flameproofing fibrous compositions. Can. pat. 774,523(Dec. 26, 1967); ABIPC 39:A1328.

A flameproof adhesive cpn. for use on paper and other matls. comprises a mixt. of a brominated fatty acid ester contg. at least 20% Br (e.g., brominated soybean oil), at least 10% of an adhesive which is immiscible with the fatty acid ester, and at least 10% of a water-insol. metal cpd. such as Sb oxide. The adhesive can be PVAc.

190. Spektor, E. M.; Gutman, A. M.; Provinteev, I. V.; Fishgoit, I. L.; Fogel', E. S. Method of making linoleum. USSR pat. 191,464(Filed Nov. 26, 1964); Publ. Izobret. no. 4:13(1967); ABIPC 38:A2389.

To increase the mech. strength and reduce the flammability of linoleum made by applg. two layers of divinylstyrene latex to the base paper (parchment paper), PS latex is added to the coating cpns., in amts. of 20-60 parts/100 parts of the divinylstyrene latex. The latter is a prod. of extensive polymerization, contg. 65% styrene, and is vulcanized with S. The cpn. for the first coating layer also contains fillers and pigments.

191. Windaus, G.; Petermann, E.; Staudemaier, P. Flameproof solid fiberboard and solid fiberboard with liners. Verpackungs-Rundschau 18, no. 5:512-14, 516, 520(May, 1967); Ger.; ABIPC 38:A3651.

The cpn. of various types of flameproof coatings for solid fiberboard is revd. along with methods for testing the flameproof props. of the coated boards. Methods for incorporating fabric liners in solid fiberboard are also mentioned. Data are presented showing the resulting improvement in strength props. (breaking length, puncture resistance, and bursting strength) and extensibility. 27 ref.

192. Wolf, M. Fire-retardant coating. U.S. pat. 3,475,199(Oct. 28, 1969); ABIPC 40:A7378.

A fire-retardant coating for paper and pbd. comprises hexamethylene tetramine, a nonvolatile heat-decomposable inorg. intumescent agent, and a binder consisting of a major proportion of hydrocarbon wax.

193. Wolf, M. Fire-retardant coating. Brit. pat. 1,144,013(March 5, 1969); ABIPC 40:A4425.

A fire-retardant coating for wallboard and other cellulosic matls. comprises an intumescent agent and a binder which includes a major portion of a hydrocarbon wax. The intumescent agent comprises hexamethylene tetramine and a heat-decomposable inorg. cpd. such as monoammonium phosphate.

PAPER

194. Albright & Wilson Ltd. Improved cellulosic materials. Fr. pat. 1,329,806(May 6, 1963); ABIPC 35:A6446.

An improved process for flameproofing cellulosic matls. with a condensation prod. of a tetrakis(hydroxymethyl)phosphonium (THP) salt and a nitrogenous cpd., which prevents the migration of the prod. to the surface of the matl. and improves its retention, consists in trg. a cellulosic matl. (e.g., paper or viscose rayon) with an aq. soln. of the THP salt, the pH of which has been adjusted to between 3 and 9.5 (preferably to 5.5-7), heating the matl. at 100-180 C. for 30-1 min. to fix the salt, then trg. it with ammonia to produce the flameproofing polymer.

195. Allgemeine Papier-Rundschau. Chemical products suitable for surface finishing of paper, paperboard, and board. Allg. Papier-Rundschau no. 5:170, 172-4, 176, 178, 180-4(Feb. 5, 1971); ABIPC 42:A5559.

This directory of trade-named chem. cpds. and formulations for paper and pbd. surface finishing trmts. lists their chem. cpn. (where known), supplier, special characs., and recommended applns. Included are surface sizing agents, coating binders and pigments, water- and fungusproofing agents, foam inhibitors, lubricants, release agents, optical brighteners, laminating and impregnating agents, lacquers, viscy. regulators, gloss and printability improvers, hot-melts and related barrier coatings, flame retardants, surfactants, dispersants, rub resistance improvers, hardeners (curing agents), adhesives, and misc. special-purpose additives.

196. Armstrong, G. K. Development of nonflammable paper constructions. NASA Contract. Rep. 1969, NASA-CR-101977, 30 pp.; Engl.; Avail. CFSTI; CA 73:A46869.

Asbestos, microfiber glass, and beta glass addns. were evald. for their low flammability and modification props. in glass based sheet devt. Results from a no. of trmts. on various substrates to evaluate possible new approaches to the mfr. of nonflammable paper are tabulated. Phosphoric acid salts (diammonium phosphate) have the ability either alone or in combination with Fluorel to fireproof cellulose in the 6.2 psia O atm.

197. Arthur, R. P.; Schweiker, G. C. Cellulosic graft polymer. Can. pat. 849,595(Aug. 18, 1970); ABIPC 41:A7583.

Cellulose in the form of wood pulp, paper, or the like is modified by graft polymerization of alpha-haloacrylonitrile in the presence of an aq. soln. of Ce ion derived, e.g., from Ce nitrate. The prod. has reduced moisture retention and flammability and improved resistance to fungi and rot.

198. Ary, D. R. Fireproof envelope. U.S. pat. 3,428,104(Feb. 18, 1969); ABIPC 40:A645.

A sheet of asbestos matl. or other fire-retardant matl. is formed into a folder having a pocket for retaining and protecting important papers. Different forms of the folder are described.

199. Badische Anilin- & Soda-Fabrik AG. Fireproofing of cellulosic fibrous material and the fireproofed material obtained. Brit. pat. 1,191,877(May 13, 1970); ABIPC 41:A5541.

This process for flameproofing paper and other cellulosic matls. is similar to that previously described in U.S. pat. 3,503,793; see Abstr. No. 204.

200. Badische Anilin- & Soda-Fabrik AG. Novel mixtures of phosphorus amides and their use for fireproofing of cellulosic fibrous material. Brit. pat. 1,221,849(Feb. 10, 1971); ABIPC 42:A6083.

The fireproofing of cellulosic matls. described in this pat. is similar to that described previously in U.S. pat. 3,563,793; see Abstr. No. 205.

201. Bloechl, W. Polyfluoroalkyl derivatives of phosphorus acids. Brit.
pat. 1,122,404(Aug. 7, 1968); ABIPC 39:A7834.

Polyfluoroalkyl phosphonic, phosphinic, thiophosphonic and thiophosphinic
acids (and their derivs.) contg. no fluorine in the alpha and beta positions
to the P are provided for use in various applns., incl. trg. textiles and paper
to render them water-, oil-, and dirt-repellent. The acid derivs. carrying polymerizable ester and amide groups are particularly useful in the trmt. of textiles
and paper. For example, 1-iodoperfluorodecane wax was reacted with vinyl phosphonic acid dichloride, and the prod. was dissolved in tetrahydrofuran and added
to ethylenimine and pyridine in ether. The pyridine hydrochloride formed was
filtered off and the solvents were evapd. The remaining oil was trd. (in
isopropyl alc.) with Na amalgam, and the prod. was sepd. from the amalgam, concd.
by evapn., and dissolved in acetone. When paper was trd. with this soln., it
became flame retardant as well as repellent to water, oil, and gasoline.

202. Brandeis, H.; Bille, H.; Pfleger, K. Fireproofing of cellulosic
fibrous material and the fireproofed material obtained. Can. pat. 845,652
(June 30, 1970); ABIPC 41:A5543.

This process for flameproofing paper and other cellulosic matls. is
similar to that previously described in U.S. pat. 3,503,793; see Abstr. No.
204.

203. Brandeis, H.; Bille, H.; Pfleger, K. Fireproofing of cellulosic
fibrous material and the fireproofed material obtained. Can. pat. 865,603
(March 9, 1971); ABIPC 42:A4011.

The method for flameproofing cellulosic fibers described in this invention
is similar to that described previously in U.S. pat. 3,563,793; see Abstr. No.
205.

204. Brandeis, H.; Pfleger, K.; Bille, H. Cellulosic fibrous materials.
U.S. pat. 3,503,793(March 31, 1970); ABIPC 41:A1487.

Paper and other cellulosic matls. are flameproofed by trmt. with certain
phosphorus amides and chloromethyl phosphonamides. Typical trmt. agents can
be prepd. by the reaction of phosphorus oxychloride, methylamine, and ethylenimine.

205. Brandeis, H.; Pfleger, K.; Bille, H. Fireproofed cellulosic material.
U.S. pat. 3,563,793(Feb. 16, 1971); ABIPC 42:A1867.

Paper and other cellulosic matls. are flameproofed by trmt. with phosphorus
amides obtained from the reaction of phosphorous oxychloride with methylamide,
ethylenimine, and ammonia in an inert org. solvent.

206. Brintzinger, H. Nonflammable decorative panel. Ger. pat. 1,817,536
(July 23, 1970); ABIPC 42:A1012.

Decorative laminates are provided in which the various paper layers are
impregnated with a mixt. consisting of 30-70% (by wt.) of MF and/or UF resins
and 70-30% of polyvinyl- and/or polyvinylidene halides and/or polyene halides
(esp. PE halide). The result is a flame-resistant laminate.

207. Brintzinger, H. Nonflammable polyester-resin decorative panel.
Ger. pat. 1,902,224(Aug. 6, 1970); ABIPC 42:A1013.

A paper/polyester-resin decorative laminate is rendered totally fire-
resistant by incorporating in the various paper layers 20-70 wt.% noncombustible
fibers, such as glass, asbestos, and/or synt. fibers (esp. polyvinyl halogen
fibers), noncombustible wet-strength agents (e.g., MF resin and/or polyvinyl
halides), and, in the case of the decorative paper layer, noncombustible pigments. In addn., the various paper layers are impregnated with 6-14% MF and/or
UF resins.

208. Bullock, J. B.; Welch, C. M. Process for reducing the flammability
and increasing the weather-resistance of fibrous organic materials. U.S. pat.
3,459,589(Aug. 5, 1969); ABIPC 40:A4069.

Paper, pbd., cellulosic textiles, and the like are rendered flame-resistant
by applg. to the fabrics polymers produced by a combination of a cpd. contg.
two or more aziridinyl groups attached to a nonmetallic atom and a cpd. contg.
S atoms having an oxidn. no. less than +6, and a methylol phosphorus cpd. For
example, the polymer can be produced from tris(1-aziridinyl)phosphine oxide,
tetrakis(hydroxymethyl)phosphonium chloride, and thiourea.

209. Carpenter, S.; Witt, E. R. Flame-resistant organic material. U.S.
pat. 3,403,049(Sept. 24, 1968); ABIPC 39:A6828.

Paper and a wide variety of other normally flammable org. matls. are rendered
flame-resistant by coating with certain halogenated org. phosphates such as
tris[2,2,2-tris(chloromethyl)ethyl] phosphate.

210. Chem 26 Paper Processing. Helping paper fight fire. Chem 26 Paper
Processing 2, no. 11:24-7(Nov., 1966); ABIPC 37:A7413.

Vi-Tard, an aq. dispersion of vinylidene chloride copolymer and Sb oxide,
marketed by National Starch & Chemical Corp., is an effective agent for flameproofing paper. Its advantages and disadvantages as compared with other com.
flameproofing agents are listed. Some potential applns. of paper trd. with Vi-
Tard, e.g., in paper honeycombs and elec. insulation, are given. Vi-Tard may
be appl. to paper by a satn. trmt., addn. at the wet-end of the paper machine,
by surface sizing, or by coating.

211. Cluett, S. L. Extensible non-combustible paper. U.S. pat. 3,148,108
(Sept. 8, 1964); ABIPC 35:A5028.

A rel. dense extensible noncombustible tough paper is formed by subjecting
a wet asbestos web (contg. asbestos fibers, asbestos dust, and not more than 5%
by wt. of adhesive binder) to the well-known Clupak process for prodg. stretch-
able paper.

212. Coates, H.; Chalkley, B. Treatment of cellulose with tetrakis(hydroxymethyl)phosphonium resins. U.S. pat. 3,236,676(Feb. 22, 1966); ABIPC 37:A1348.

Paper and other cellulosic matls. are flameproofed by trmt. with a cpn.
consisting of an aq. soln. of a tetrakis(hydroxymethyl)phosphonium salt having
a pH of 3-9.5, drying the trd. matl., heating, then trg. with ammonia.

213. Coates, H.; Chalkley, B. Treatment of cellulose with tetrakis(hydroxy-methyl)phosphonium resins. Can. pat. 708,878(May 4, 1965); ABIPC 36:A1977.

This process for flameproofing paper and other cellulosic matls. is similar to that described in Brit. pat. 938,990; see Abstr. No. 186 in Biblio. Series No. 185, Suppl. I, Flameproofing, 1965.

214. Credali, L. The properties of polyamide fiber and paper NT-1. Mater. Plast. Elast. 32, no. 8:835-8(1966); Ital.; Ref. Zh., Khim. no. 8:abstr. S1059 (April, 25, 1967); ABIPC 38:A1838.

The Du Pont NT-1 polyamide fiber (the presumed mol. structure of which is given) retains its mech. strength at temps. 250-300 C. At 285 C. its tensile strength is 50% of the initial (at 20 C.). The fiber can withstand oxidn. for prolonged time, can be ignited only with a direct flame, and extinguishes itself when the flame is removed. It is carbonized at about 400 C. As compared with nylon 66, dacron, and similar fibers, the NT-1 fiber has a higher resistance to abrasion, higher hardness, tensile strength, dimensional stability, higher resistance to chemicals such as various reagents and solvents, and higher resistance to irradiation with beta and gamma rays. The technol. of making paper from the NT-1 fiber is described, and the mech. props. of such paper are compared with those of quality rag paper. Excellent elec. insulation props. of the NT-1 synt. paper and its high resistance to heat, make it esp. well suited for use as insulating matl. in elec. motors and transformers (its service life at 220 deg. is over 10 yr.).

215. Dahms, R. H. Plasticized phenolic resin impregnation system. U.S. pat. 3,537,952(Nov. 3, 1970); ABIPC 41:A7927.

A resin cpn. for use in the prodn. of paper laminates having good elec. props., high fire retardancy, and rel. low temp. punchability comprises two different phenolic resins and a compatible halo aryl phosphate. One of the resins is a PF resole, the other is another resole formed using a substituted phenol derived from the reaction of phenol with cyclopentadiene dimers.

216. Davis, J. C. Fire protection for paper rolls. U.S. pat. 3,261,460 (July 19, 1966); ABIPC 37:A5356.

A fire-retarding waterproof wrapper for paper rolls consists of a laminate of paper and metal foil.

217. Davis, R. A. Fire-retardancy of lignocellulosic materials by phos-phorylating chlorinated or brominated lignocellulosics. U.S. pat. 3,459,588(Aug. 5, 1969); ABIPC 40:A4384.

The fire-retardant props. of paper, pbd., and other LC matls. are improved by chlorinating or brominating the matl. and then phosphorylating with a tri-alkyl or triaryl phosphite or phosphonate such as triethyl phosphite.

218. Demott, D. N. Fire-resistant cellulosic materials and a method of preparation. U.S. pat. 3,558,596(Jan. 26, 1971); ABIPC 42:A645.

A cellulosic matl. such as paper or textile is rendered fire resistant by reaction with a vinylphosphonate.

219.   Domovs, K. B.; Lee, W. K.; Tesoro, G. C.   Process for flameproofing polymeric materials. Can. pat. 798,217(Nov. 5, 1968); ABIPC 40:A2600.

Paper and other cellulosic matls. are flameproofed by trg. the matl. with certain N-contg. phosphonates and cross-linking the phosphonate in situ with a suitable agent. For example, the phosphonate can be prepd. by reacting a halogenated phosphonate such as bis(2-chloroethyl)(2-chloroethyl)phosphonate with a nitrogenous cpd. such as ethylenediamine. The cross-linking agent can be tris(1-aziridinyl)phosphine oxide.

220.   Dow Chemical Co.   Fireproofing cellulosic material.   Brit. pat. 1,063,273(March 30, 1967); ABIPC 38:A4076.

Paper and other cellulosic matls. are flameproofed by trmt. with a cpn. incl. thiourea or a related cpd., and tris(1-aziridinyl)phospine oxide.

221.   Elmer, C.; Mestdagh, J. J.   Self-extinguishing phenolic resin compositions and laminates prepared therefrom. U.S. pat. 3,352,744(Nov. 14, 1967); ABIPC 38:A9709.

A flame-retardant laminate of use in elec. applns. is prepd. from paper sheets by using a resin prepd. by reacting a phenol with styrene, reacting the prod. with a vegetable drying oil, reacting this prod. with an aldehyde, and then reacting the resin so formed with a chlorinated polyphenyl and with a phosphate such as bis(beta-bromoethyl) beta-chloroethyl phosphate.

222.   Esso Research & Engineering Co.   Compositions containing lithium and sodium silicates. Brit. pat. 1,007,481(Oct. 13, 1965); ABIPC 37:A2122.

A cpn. for waterproofing or flameproofing paper or the like comprises an aq. soln. of Li and Na silicates present in amts. such as to provide a molar ratio of Li oxide to Na oxide to Si dioxide of 0.75-1.0:0.05-0.25:2.5-5.0.

223.   Esso Research & Engineering Co.   Compositions containing lithium silicates. Brit. pat. 1,007,482(Oct. 13, 1965); ABIPC 37:A2123.

A cpn. for flameproofing or waterproofing or the like comprises an aq. soln. of Li silicate in which the molar ratio of Li oxide to Si dioxide is from 1:2 to 1:6.3.

224.   Fikentscher, R.; Brandeis, H.; Bille, H.   New halomethylphosphonic acid bisamides and process for flameproofing cellulosic fibrous material therewith. Brit. pat. 1,126,259(Sept. 5, 1968); ABIPC 39:A8830.

Paper and other cellulosic matls. are flameproofed by heat trmt. after impregnation with a halomethylphosphonic acid such as chloromethylphosphonic acid diamide.

225.   Frohning, H.   Phenolic resin composition and paper impregnated therewith. Brit. pat. 1,157,397(July 9, 1969); ABIPC 40:A6320.

A method of making a resin-impregnated paper sheet suitable for use as a core sheet in a fire-resistant laminate or as a fireproof facing sheet or barrier

sheet on a combustible wood-based matl. involves impregnating the paper with a
PF resin soln. to which has been added 0.05-0.15 mole of phosphoric acid per
mole of phenol, at least 3 moles of ammonia per mole of phosphoric acid, and as
much HCHO as needed for at least 1 mole HCHO per mole of ammonia to be present in
a form not bound by the phenol.

226. Goldstein, I. S. Method of flameproofing cellulosic materials. U.S.
pat. 3,479,211(Nov. 18, 1969); ABIPC 40:A8429.

Cellulosic matls. such as paper are flameproofed by impregnation with a
thermosetting resin comprising, for example, the reaction prod. of dicyandiamide,
trimethylolmelamine, phosphoric acid, and HCHO.

227. Goldstein, I. S. Method of flameproofing cellulosic materials. Can.
pat. 846,756(July 14, 1970); ABIPC 41:A7900.

Paper and the like cellulosic matls. are flameproofed by incorporating in
the matl. particles of a water-insol. thermoset resin formed from a P-contg.
cpd. and a N-contg. cpd., such as a resin formed from dicyandiamide, phosphoric
acid, HCHO, and melamine.

228. Graff, P. Nonwoven fabrics and paper as outer clothing. Melliand
Textilber. 49, no. 1:51-6(Jan., 1968); Ger.; ABIPC 39:A1995.

Flg. a rev. of the introduction of paper and nonwoven fabric clothing in
Europe and the U.S.A., mfg. techniques for filament-reinforced papers and the
various types of nonwoven fabrics are outlined along with some of the props.
(mech. strength props., drapability, handle, moisture permeability, abrasion
resistance) of these matls. Printing, flameproofing, and finishing are also
discussed, along with techniques (sewing, gluing, taping, pattern cutting) used
in the mfr. of clothing items. Fashion trends are also briefly examd.

229. Gutierrez de Tena, A. J. Treatment of paper. Invest. Tec. Papel 6,
no. 20:443-75(April, 1969); Span.; ABIPC 40:A4804.

This is a gen. rev. of the coating, impregnation, and laminating of paper.
Emphasis is placed on the various types of impregnating agents (paraffin wax,
microcryst. wax, wax/synt. resin mixts., synt. waxes, bitumen, synt. resin
emulsions, plasticizers, flameproofing agents, fungicides, bactericides, and
insecticides), coating cpns., and laminating adhesives used.

230. Hadley, T. A.; Vanevenhoven, R. J. Manufacture of cellulosic product.
Can. pat. 777,090(Jan. 30, 1968); ABIPC 39:A2527.

In the process of improving the flame resistance of cellulosic matls. such
as paper by impregnation with ammonium sulfamate, the aging resistance of the
matl. is improved by incl. urea in the impregnating cpn.

231. Harrington, J. A. Fire-resistant paper-base epoxy resin laminates.
U.S. pat. 3,378,434(April 16, 1968); ABIPC 39:A3488.

A fire-resistant paper-base resinous laminate comprises a no. of sheets
of paper impregnated and bonded with a solid binder derived from a resin cpn.

contg. a brominated bis-phenol-epichlorohydrin epoxide, up to an equal amt. by wt. of a bis-phenol-epichlorohydrin epoxide, a halogenated anhydride, and antimony trioxide.

232. Harrington, J. A. Fire-resistant paper-base epoxy resin laminates. Can. pat. 791,206(July 30, 1968); ABIPC 39:A6224.

A fire-resistant laminate of elec. grade consists of a no. of sheets of paper impregnated and bonded together with a resin cpn. contg. a brominated bis-phenol-epichlorohydrin epoxide and a bis-phenol-epichlorohydrin epoxide, together with a halogenated anhydride such as chlorendic anhydride, and Sb trioxide.

233. Hooker Chemical Corp. Fire retardant bituminous composition. Brit. pat. 1,057,115(Feb. 1, 1967); ABIPC 38:A2903.

A fire-retardant cpn. for use in various coated and impregnated papers, roofing matls., etc., comprises a bituminous matl., a halogenated cpd. such as perchloropentacyclodecane, and a halogenated hydrocarbon solvent, such as trichloroethylene.

234. Hooker Chemical Corp. Flame retardant composition and process. Brit. pat. 1,049,341(Nov. 23, 1966); ABIPC 38:A3811.

A cpn. useful in flameproofing cellulosic matl. such as paper comprises a polyvinyl halide-contg. latex, a resinous precondensate formed by the reaction of tetrakis(hydroxymethyl)phosphonium chloride, urea, HCHO, and Sb oxide. The urea and HCHO are in the form of a resin as precondensate. The latex can be a PVC latex.

235. Hooker Chemical Corp. Flame-retardant composition and process. Brit. pat. 1,057,829(Feb. 8, 1967); ABIPC 38:A4078.

Paper and other cellulosic matls. are flameproofed by trmt. with a cpn. comprising a polyvinyl halide such as PVC, a resinous precondensate formed by the reaction of a tetrakis(hydroxy-organo)phosphonium halide other than THPC, urea, and HCHO; and Sb oxide.

236. Hovd, S. Stable phenol-formaldehyde resin solution for the preparation of fire-resistant laminates. Can. pat. 864,011(Feb. 16, 1971); ABIPC 42:A2158.

Paper laminates of improved fire resistance are mfd. using as laminating cpn. a PF resin soln. contg. certain phosphates such as ammonium methyl phosphates, ammonium bromide, a 1-4 C alkanol, and water.

237. Ishihara, S.; Maku, T. Studies on fireproofing treatments for composite wood. (1) Fireproof treatment of wood and paper by means of primary condensation products of melamine-formaldehyde combined with phosphoric acid. Wood Res. (Kyoto) no. 42:13-39(Dec., 1967); Jap.; ABIPC 39:A3876.

Samples of sliced hinoki veneer (Chamaecyparis obtusa) 0.34 mm. thick and of filter paper (0.26 mm.) were padded with an aq. soln. of MF-phosphoric acid condensate (MFP), then dried and cured 30 min. at 130 C. to insolubilize the absorbed resin (which is a modified melamine acid colloid of the kind widely used in wet-strength paper). Several formulations of MFP differing in HCHO:melamine: phosphoric acid ratio were compared with each other and with water-sol. phosphates, such as triguanidine phosphate and diammonium hydrogen phosphate. Compared with other flame retardants, only a small amt. of MFP was needed to impart flame resistance, viz., 3.0-11.2% for the veneer and 6.1-12.0% for filter paper. None of the trd. specimens showed afterglow. The aq. trg. solns. are fairly stable at pH 5-8. By varying the molar ratio of phosphoric acid to melamine, the pyrolysis temp. of wood and cellulose can be changed; similarly, the flameproofing effect can be controlled by varying the molar ratio of HCHO to melamine. 23 ref.

238. Kenaga, D. L. Method of treating paper with ethylenimine derivatives using a boron trifluoride-amine complex catalyst. U.S. pat. 3,428,484(Feb. 18, 1969); ABIPC 40:A823.

Paper is sized and simult. improved in wet and dry strength, flame resistance, and folding endurance by trmt. with an ethylenimine deriv. and a boron trifluoride-amine complex in an anhydrous system. For example, the trmt. cpds. can be tris(1-aziridinyl) phosphine oxide and a boron trifluoride/ hexamethylenetetramine complex.

239. Kuchta, J. M.; Furno, A. L.; Martindill, G. H. Flammability of fabrics and other materials in oxygen-enriched atmospheres. I. Ignition temperatures and flame spread rates. Fire Technol. 5, no. 3:203-16(1969); CA 72:A80202.

The effects of O enrichment on ignition temp. and flame spread rates for combustible solids were investigated. The min. autoignition temps. were lowest for cotton sheeting (385 C.) and highest for PVC sheets (560 C.) in air at 1 atm. Hot-plate ignition temps. were higher, but decreased with an O concn. of 42% or more. Values at O at 1 atm. were equal or less than those in air at 6 atm. In 21% or more O atm., ignition temps. correlated with the inverse of O partial pressures raised to a fraction power. Most matls. did not propagate flame when ignited at a 45 deg. angle in air at 1 atm., but all propagated flames in O at 0.2 atm. or more. The flame spread hazard was greater with paper and cotton sheeting than with rubber sheeting and plastics, and was the greatest with napped matls., e.g., blanket wool. Flame spread rates depended more upon O concn. than upon total pressure.

240. Kuchta, J. M.; Litchfield, E. L.; Furno, A. L. Flammability of materials in hyperbaric atmospheres. U.S. Atomic Energy Comm. 1967, Rept.-4016, 59 p.; Avail. CFSTI; CA 71:A93209.

To evaluate the fire hazards of combustion solids in hyperbaric atm. hotplate ignition temps., flame spread rates, and min. ignition energies were detd. for cotton sheeting, cotton sheeting trd. with fire retardants, cotton balls, paper drapes, conductive rubber sheeting, blanket wool, PVC sheet, Plexiglas sheet, cellulose sheet, wood strips and dowels, and a Nomex fabric. Air, O, and various O-N mixts. were employed at 1-6 atm. Detns. for selected combustibles were made in O at reduced pressures. Matls. trd. with certain fire retardants ignite in O-enriched atm. at lower temps. than untrd. matls.

241.   Lard, E. W.; Orgell, C. W.   Process for flameproofing combustible materials.   U.S. pat. 3,540,892(Nov. 17, 1970); ABIPC 41:A8948.

A method of flameproofing paper or the like involves coating it with vermiculite by dipping the paper in a vermiculite suspension and then drying the prod.   The vermiculite suspension is prepd. by soaking vermiculite in aq. NaCl, water washing, steeping in concd. lithium chloride, water washing, and exfoliating with water.

242.   Le Blanc, R. B.   Treatment of cellulosic material with APO-thiourea flame resistance and the resulting material.   U.S. pat. 3,376,160(April 2, 1968); ABIPC 39:A2168.

Cellulosic matls. such as textiles and paper are rendered flame-retardant by trmt. with a cpn. incl. thiourea and tris(1-aziridinyl)phosphine oxide in a mole ratio of 0.3-3.0:1, fld. by curing at an elevated temp.

243.   Le Blanc, R. B.; Symm, R. H.   Treatment of cellulosic materials with a polyaziridinylphosphoramide and a sulfamide.   U.S. pat. 3,409,463(Nov. 5, 1968); ABIPC 39:A7851.

Paper, pbd., and other cellulosic matls. are flameproofed and dimensionally stabilized by trmt. with a cpn. contg. a polyaziridinylphosphoramide and a sulfamide derived from ammonia or a primary alkylamine.   For example, the cpn. can contain tris(1-aziridinyl)phosphine oxide and a sulfamide prepd. by reaction of sulfuryl chloride and excess ammonia.

244.   Lewin, M.   Fire-proofing lignocellulosic structures with bromine and chlorine compositions.   U.S. pat. 3,150,919(Sept. 29, 1964); ABIPC 35:A5093.

A process is provided for forming fire-resistant LC matls., such as pulp, paper, wood-particle board, and the like.   The LC matl. is trd. with a liquid reaction medium incl. a metal bromide, Cl is introduced into the reaction medium to liberate the Br from the bromide and effect bromination of the lignin component of the LC up to a Br content of 2.7-8% by wt. of the LC, and the LC is sepd. from the reaction medium.   The reaction medium can also incl. dissolved buffer flameproofing agents such as ammonium phosphates.

245.   Manning, J. H.; Atkins, J. W.; Moore, M.   Process for preparation of fibrous water-insoluble cellulose sulfate salts.   U.S. pat. 3,567,708(March 2, 1971); ABIPC 42:A3299.

A process for prodg. a flame-resistant water-insol. cellulose sulfate salt comprises trg. cellulose (e.g., wood pulp or the like) with DMSO or a DMSO/DMF mixt. in the presence of sulfur trioxide in complex with DMSO or DMF, neutg. the trd. matl., water-washing, and deswelling with a salt contg. a polyvalent cation, such as aluminum sulfate.   The trd. matl. can be formed into flame-resistant paper.

246.   Minnesota Mining & Mfg. Co.   Sheet materials.   Brit. pat. 1,042,597 (Sept. 14, 1966); ABIPC 38:A1592.

This sheet is generally similar to the paper described in Brit. pat. 1,042,596 (cf. ABIPC 38:A1590), except that no reactant other than that within the capsules is required, and the sheet is not necessarily a recording paper. Besides marking cpds., the capsules can include a shoe polish, an adhesive, a perfume, a fire retardant, or other matl.

247.   Minnesota Mining & Mfg. Co.   Sheet materials.   Brit. pat. 1,042,598 (Sept. 14, 1966); ABIPC 38:A1593.

This invention covers related aspects of the matl. presented in Brit. pat. 1,042,597; see preceding abstr.

248.   Monsanto Co.   Flame-retardant fibrous cellulosic materials.   Brit. pat. 1,184,878(March 18, 1970); ABIPC 41:A3476.

Paper and the like cellulosic prods. are rendered flame-retardant by incl. in them certain ammonium polyphosphates.   In the case of paper, the poly-phosphates can be added at the wet end, or to the finished paper.

249.   Monsanto Co.   Halogenated esters, their production and use.   Brit. pat. 1,062,463(March 22, 1967); ABIPC 38:A3813.

Paper and other matls. are flameproofed by trmt. with a poly(2,3-dihaloalkyl) ester of an acid such as an aromatic polycarboxylic acid.   A typical cpd. claimed by the present invention is bis(2,3-dibromopropyl) phthalate.

250.   Monsanto Co.   Improvements in and relating to the fireproofing of polyamide shaped articles.   Brit. pat. 1,214,554(Dec. 2, 1970); ABIPC 42:A5036.

A process for the prepn. of a flameproof dimensionally stable flexible aromatic polyamide shaped article (particularly fibers) comprises heating the article to a temp. below its softening point and at or above the temp. required for reaction with a vaporous oxidant which is a halide or oxyhalide of the nonmetallic elts. of Group IV, V, or VI of the Periodic table, and reacting the article with the oxidant to form the desired article.   For example, flock fibers of poly-m-phenylene (m-benzamido) terephthalamide were trd. with sulfur mono-chloride at 367 C. for 1 hr.   Subsequently, the trd. fibers were formed into paper by std. methods and the paper was shown to be flameproof and dimensionally stable.

251.   Morida, I.; Ohda, H.   Fire-retardant treatment of paper and wood materials.   Jap. pat. 70 31,689(Oct. 14, 1970); CA 75:A22857.

A mixt. of ammonium dihydrogen phosphate, or ammonium sulfamate and a reaction product of dicyandiamide (I) and monomethyl phosphate (II), mono(2-chloroethyl) phosphate or monoethyl phosphate, or their methylolation prods. is a flame-retardant for wood and paper.   A cedarwood specimen impregnated successively with solns. of monomethyl phosphate and methylolated (I)-(II) prod., ignited at 360 C. and had burning time 25 sec.

252.   Pande, K. C.   Fire-retardant cellulosic compositions.   U.S. pat. 3,560,479(Feb. 2, 1971); ABIPC 42:A1874.

Reaction between cellulose and a bis-beta,beta-(dialkylphosphono) propionic acid deriv. results in integral attachment of the deriv. to the cellulose polymer chain and provides the cellulose with permanent flame-retardant props. Paper and cellulosic textiles can both be trd. in this manner.

253. Pande, K. C. N-Hydroxymethyl-bis-beta,beta-(dialkylphosphono)propion-amides for flameproofing of cellulose materials. Ger. Offen. 2,050,673(April 29, 1971); CA 75:A37856.

254. Papiermacher. To the moon with German paper. Papiermacher 19, special no.:200-2(Dec. 13, 1969); Ger.; ABIPC 41:A3207.

A brief rept. is presented on the devt. of a special fire-resistant paper by Papierfabrik Scheufelen (West Germany) for the U.S. space program. The paper is used in maps and writing paper aboard spaceships.

255. Perstorp AB. Process for obtaining decorative laminate products with good flame resistance. Fr. pat. 1,577,877(June 30, 1969); ABIPC 41:A4944.

Decorative laminates of resin-impregnated paper are rendered fire-resistant through incorporation of a layer coated with a cpn. incorporating an org. Cl cpd. contg. at least 50% by wt. of Cl (PVC, PVdC, etc.); a metallic oxide which forms, when reacted with HCl, a chloride undergoing sublimation at a temp. under 400 C. (Al or Sb trioxide); and a resin binder (e.g., a MF resin binder). The laminates are constructed such that the specially coated layer contacts the decorative surface.

256. Peterson, G. J. Flameproofing composition, method and article containing same. U.S. pat. 3,305,431(Feb. 21, 1967); ABIPC 38:A2163.

A flameproof adhesive cpn. for use in making paper laminates comprises a mixt. of at least about 10% by wt. of a water-insol. salt of As, Sb, Bi, or Sn, at least 15% of a brominated vegetable oil, and at least 10% of PVAc adhesive.

257. Read, A. E.; Baxandall, J. S. Improvements in flame, rot and water-proofing fibrous materials. Brit. pat. 1,136,049(Dec. 11, 1968); ABIPC 40:A1335.

A cellulosic matl. such as paper or textile matl., is waterproofed and rendered flame resistant with a cpn. incl. a neut. or alk. emulsion of a wax, a chlorinated or brominated paraffin wax, an org. deriv. of Ti or Zr or Al dissolved in the wax phase, and antimony phosphate and oxide. The org. metal deriv. can be butyl titanate. The cpn. can also include a rotproofing agent such as pentachlorophenol laurate.

258. Rogovin, Z. A.; Tyuganova, M. A.; Kryazhev, Y. G.; Zharova, T. J. Process for flameproofing cellulosic articles. Ger. pat. 1,289,024(Exam. copy Feb. 13, 1969); ABIPC 41:A5566.

A process for wash-resistant flameproofing of cellulosic matls. (incl. cellulosic fibers, fabrics, paper, and films) involves trmt. in succession with aq. solns. of the sulfuric acid ester of 4-(beta-hydroxyethylsulfonyl)-2-amino-anisole, nitrous acid, and 2-methyl-5-vinylpyridine in the presence of ferrous salts. The resulting cellulose copolymers are trd. with a 0.5-1% phosphoric acid soln. at 20-60 C.

259. Rogovin, Z. A.; Tyuganova, M. A.; Kryazhev, Y. G.; Zharova, T. J. Process for production of nonflammable cellulose graft copolymer. U.S. pat. 3,391,096(July 2, 1968); ABIPC 39:A4961.

Paper and other cellulosic matls. are flameproofed by graft copolymerizing the cellulose with poly(2-methyl-5-vinyl pyridine), then trg. with dil. phosphoric acid at 20-60 C.

260. Rogovin, Z. A.; Tyuganova, M. A.; Kryazhev, Y. G.; Zharova, T. J. Process for production of nonflammable cellulose materials. Brit. pat. 1,022,083 (March 9, 1966); ABIPC 37:A7050.

Paper and other cellulosic matls. are flameproofed by chemically modifying the cellulose to include a basic group (primary amino or pyridine), then trg. the modified matl. with phosphoric acid. Preferably, the modification consists of graft polymerization with poly(2-methyl-5-vinyl pyridine).

261. Satonaka, S.; Kobayashi, S.; Kawashima, Y. Fire retardation of wood. Res. Bull. Coll. Expt. Forest Hokkaido Univ. 25, no. 1:235-64(1967); Jap.; ABIPC 40:A1264.

A thermoanal. study was made of the pyrolysis (combustion) of whole wood, xylan, lignin, and cellulose (filter paper) with and without flame-retardant chem. trmts. Heat degradation started in the order xylan, lignin, cellulose. Lignin showed considerable heat resistance, retaining 36% of its original wt. at 450 C. The pyrolysis of filter paper trd. with diammonium hydrogen phosphate (DHP) started at 160 C.; the sheet retained its original shape and 29% of its wt. Of several flame retardants evald., DHP, ''Minalith,'' ''Pyresote,'' and ''D:P'' (dicyandiamide + phosphoric acid) were the most effective; chlorinated paraffin was intermediate; trimethyl, triethyl, triphenyl, and tricresyl phosphates were little effective. The combustion test was standardized by devising a special wind-protected burner into which the paper test strip (6 x 13 cm.) was pulled by remote control at a flame height of 2 cm. Gases from retardant-trd. paper were anald. by gas chromat. Effective chemicals decreased the amt. of combustible gas and increased the amt. of water generated. There was little ammonia in the gas from paper trd. with DHP. 26 ref.

262. Seeliger, W. Process for manufacture of flameproof paper. Ger. pat. 1,214,986(Oct. 27, 1966); ABIPC 39:A1614.

A process for the mfr. of flameproof paper involves impregnating 100 parts (by wt.) of paper with an aq. soln. of 3 to 25 parts (preferably 5 to 22 parts) of the ammonium or amine salts of the sulfuric acid esters of alpha-hydroxy-carboxylic acid amides (such as alpha-hydroxyisobutyric acid amide) along with other known flameproofing agents, if necessary.

263. Skanska Attikfabriken AB. Resin-impregnated material containing a fire retardant. Brit. pat. 989,140(April 14, 1965); ABIPC 36:A6884.

In the mfr. of decorative laminates from resin-impregnated paper, fire resistance is imparted to the prod. by incl. in the resin a phosphate of an amine having a C:N atom ratio of 1:1 to 3:1, such as a reaction prod. of ethanolamine and phosphoric acid.

264. Strother, G. W., Jr. Leachproof fire-resistant complex for cellulosic substrates. U.S. pat. 3,565,679(Feb. 23, 1971); ABIPC 42:A1879.

Cellulosic matls. such as wood and paper are provided with increased fire resistance by trmt. with an aq. soln. of a complex of a polyalkylene-polyamine (e.g., PEI) and a condensation prod. of phosphorus pentoxide and ammonia.

265. Sunden, N. B. Method for the manufacture of products of resin-impregnated, fibrous material. U.S. pat. 3,383,267(May 14, 1968); ABIPC 39:A3503.

This method for use in the mfr. of decorative laminates is similar to that described in Brit. pat. 989,140; see Abstr. No. 263.

266. Sunden, N. B. Process for the manufacture of synthetic resin laminates. Ger. pat. 1,546,445(Exam. copy Dec. 11, 1969); ABIPC 41:A7948.

This process for the mfr. of decorative laminates is similar to that described in U.S. pat. 3,383,267; see preceding abstr.

267. Sutker, B. J.; Mazzarella, E. D. Manufacturing and marketing aspects of flame-resistant paper. Tappi 49, no. 12:138-44A(Dec., 1966); ABIPC 37:A7420.

Rating of fire resistance varies with test methods employed and actual conditions of use. The mechanism by which flame resistance is imparted to a combustible substance depends on the specific chemicals used. Flame-resistant papers can be made on conventional pmkg. equipment. Std. techniques may be used to apply various flameproofing formulations; wet-end addn., saturation, coating, size-press, spray, and combinations of these procedures have been used successfully. These are discussed in terms of suitability for specific prod. applns. and the characs. of available chem. systems. The marketing problem of such papers represents a balance of cost vs. performance. Elec. insulation, display matls., and building prods. are examples of growing outlets for flame-resistant papers. Stricter fire codes require the use of more flame-resistant matls. than before. New uses, together with the desired props. of trd. papers, are discussed.

268. Temin, S. C. Organic phosphorus esters and polyesters. U.S. pat. 3,179,522(April 20, 1965); ABIPC 36:A4969.

A cpn. for imparting flame resistance to cellulosic matls. (e.g., paper, cotton textiles, wood) consists of an aq. soln. contg. 1-20% by wt. of an org. water-sol. poly(phosphonate-phosphinate) cpd. such as poly[phosphinicobis-(methyl)]phenylphoshonate.

269. Volkova, T. P.; Voronovskaya, G. A.; Dubrovskii, V. A.; Rychko, V. A. Paper from basalt fiber. Bumazh. Prom. no. 6:10-11(June, 1965); Russ.; ABIPC 36:A4085.

Samples of paper contg. from 0 to 80% of fine basaltic fibers (diam. 0.9-1 micrometers) were prepd. on a lab. sheet-forming machine by the ``wet process.'' Prior to sheet formation, the fiber suspensions were refined in a hollander, either separately (at a basalt fiber consistency of not more than 1.5%) or jointly with cellulose fibers (in this case a suspension of higher consistency could be used). The dried sheets, conditioned at 20 C. and 65% RH, were tested for their phys. and mech. props. The addn. of basalt fibers increased the absorbability of paper and the rate of filtration through it, as a result of its higher porosity. The hygroscopicity of the paper was greatly reduced. Thus, at a basalt fiber content in the blend of 16%, it was reduced by 15%, the moisture content of conditioned sheets was 0.3%, as compared with 8.5% for 100% cellulose paper. Upon ignition, the basalt fiber-contg. sheets retained their original form, and at a high content of such fibers, the paper became flame resistant. The heat-insulating capacity of the papers increased in proportion to the content of basalt fibers. The mech. strength of the papers was, however, considerably lowered by the addn. of basalt fibers. It could be improved markedly by the addn. of org. binders, such as PVA emulsion or PF resin. It is suggested that basalt fiber papers could, in many instances, substitute for prods. made of glass fibers.

270. Wagner, G. M. Composition and process for treating cellulosic materials to make them flame-retardant. U.S. pat. 3,243,391(March 29, 1966); ABIPC 37:A2132.

A cpn. for flameproofing paper or the like cellulosic matl. comprises a resinous precondensate of a tetrakis(hydroxyorgano)phosphonium halide, urea, and HCHO in a molar ratio of 3-14:1:1.5-2.5 in combination with Sb oxide and a polyvinyl halide such as PVC.

271. Wagner, G. M. Flame retardant composition and process. Can. pat. 816,753(July 1, 1969); ABIPC 40:A7375.

A flameproofing cpn. for use on paper and the like comprises a resinous precondensate of urea, HCHO, and tetrakis(alpha-hydroxyorgano)phosphonium halide, where the organo-substituent is other than methyl when the halide is the chloride, in combination with a PVC latex and Sb oxide.

272. Wagner, G. M. Flameproofing composition and process. Can. pat. 741,223(Aug. 23, 1966); ABIPC 37:A5983.

A cellulosic matl. such as paper is flameproofed by contacting the matl. with a tetrakis(alpha-hydroxyorgano)phosphonium halide to deposit a flame-retardant amt. of the phosphonium halide on the matl., then contacting the resulting matl. with a N-contg. curing agent such as ammonia.

273. Wagner, G. M. Flameproofing of cellulosic material. U.S. pat. 3,219,478(Nov. 23, 1965); ABIPC 36:A8130.

A process for flameproofing a cellulosic matl. such as paper or textile involves drying and curing the matl. after impregnation with an aq. dispersion contg. a hydroxymethylphosphonium chloride cpd., a triazine or dimethylol cyclic alkylene urea such as trimethylolmelamine, thiourea or urea, an alkyl amine such as triethanolamine, a PVC resin, and Sb oxide.

274. Wagner, G. M. Flame-retarding methylol-phosphorus nitrogen-containing solutions. Can. pat. 729,258(March 1, 1966); ABIPC 37:A2133.

This cpn. for flameproofing paper and other cellulosic matls. is similar
to that described in U.S. pat. 3,101,278; see Abstr. No. 264 in Biblio. Series
No. 185, Suppl. I, Flameproofing, 1965.

275. Wagner, G. M. Method of flameproofing. Can. pat. 728,608(Feb. 22,
1966); ABIPC 37:A1362.

A process for flameproofing cellulosic matls. such as textiles and paper
comprises impregnating the matl. with an aq. soln. of a tetrakis(alpha-hydroxyorgano)phosphonium chloride cpd., a water-sol. cyclic copolymerizable N-contg.
cpd. (e.g., trimethylol melamine), an acid polymerization catalyst, and urea
or thiourea; heating until the copolymer which is formed in situ is insol. in
ammonium hydroxide; and then contacting the resin-impregnated matl. with
ammonia.

276. Wagner, G. M. Polyvinyl chloride methylol-phosphorous fire-retardant
dispersion. Can. pat. 733,562(May 3, 1966); ABIPC 37:A3684.

This cpn. and process for flameproofing cellulosic textiles are similar to
those described in U.S. pat. 3,219,478; see Abstr. No. 273.

277. Wagner, G. M. Polyvinyl chloride methylol-phosphorus nitrogen-
containing dispersion cloth impregnants. Can. pat. 729,257(March 1, 1966);
ABIPC 37:A2917.

Paper and cellulosic textiles are flameproofed by impregnation with an aq.
dispersion of a hydroxymethyl phosphonium chloride cpd., a water-sol. cyclic
N-contg. cpd. such as dimethylol ethylene urea, a water-sol. tertiary amine
such as triethanolamine, urea, and a PVC resin, then drying and curing the trd.
matl.

278. Wagner, G. M. Process for flameproofing cellulosic textile material.
U.S. pat. 3,310,420(March 21, 1967); ABIPC 38:A2070.

This is similar to U.S. pat. 3,310,419 (see flg. abstr.), the alk. stabilizer
being eliminated and the cpn. incl. an acid-releasing catalyst such as Mg
chloride or a tertiary amine hydrochloride.

279. Wagner, G. M. Process for treating cellulosic material with flameproofing composition. U.S. pat. 3,310,419(March 21, 1967); ABIPC 38:A2071.

A process for flameproofing cellulosic matls. such as textiles and paper
comprises impregnating the matl. with a polymerizable cpn. consisting of a
tetrakis(alpha-hydroxyorgano)phosphonium halide, a water-sol. cyclic N-contg.
cpd. such as trimethylol melamine, a carbamic acid deriv. such as urea, and an
alk. stabilizer such as NaOH, heating the impregnated matl. so as to partially
polymerize the impregnating cpn. and render it ammonia-insol., and then
contacting the impregnated matl. with ammonia so as to completely cure the
impregnating cpn. and render it water-insol.

280. Wagner, G. M.; Hoch, P. E. Flame-retardant methylol-phosphorus
nitrogen-containing compositions. Can. pat. 734,033(May 10, 1966); ABIPC
37:A3685.

This process for flameproofing cellulosic fabrics is similar to that described in U.S. pat. 3,101,279; see Abstr. No. 265 in Biblio. Series No. 185, Suppl. I, Flameproofing, 1965.

281. Wohnsiedler, H. P. Cationic phosphorus-containing wet strength resin colloid and paper having a content thereof. U.S. pat. 3,305,436(Feb. 21, 1967); ABIPC 38:A2103.

Wet-strength paper is prepd. by use of an aq. acid soln. of thermosetting polyhydroxymethyl tris [(4,6-diamino-s-triazine-2)-yl]ethyl phosphine oxide in cationic colloidal state. The soln. can be used to treat paper, or as a stock additive. The flammability of the paper is also decreased.

282. Wygant, J. C.; Prill, E. J.; Anderson, R. M. Flame-retardant compounds and compositions containing halogen. U.S. pat. 3,236,659(Feb. 22, 1966); ABIPC 38:A2105.

A cpn. of use in flameproofing paper, pbd., pulp, and the like comprises a major portion of synt. resin such as PS and a poly(2,3-dihaloalkyl) carboxylic ester of a polycarboxylic acid, such as a bis(2,3-dibromopropyl) carboxylic ester of a phthalic acid.

PLASTICS

283. Beinarovich, A. V.; Orlova, E. M.; Voskresenskii, V. A.; Pastukhov, V. N. Method of obtaining modified materials based on cellulose nitrate. USSR pat. 266,206(Filed April 25, 1967); Publ. Otkryt. Izobret. 47, no. 11:99(March 17, 1970); ABIPC 41:A3468.

To improve the flame resistance of CN matls., such matls. are trd. with tri-(2,3-dibromopropyl) phosphate or with di-(2,3-dibromopropyl) allyl phosphate.

284. Brinegar, W. C.; Di Pietro, J. Flame-retardant cellulose acetate articles. U.S. pat. 3,597,243(Aug. 3, 1971); ABIPC 42:A7125.

Flame-retardant films and filaments are formed from a CDA soln. which also contains halogenated alkyl phosphate, a second additive such as a halogenated paraffin or dicumyl peroxide, and a third additive such as triphenyl phosphate.

285. Brinegar, W. C.; Di Pietro, J. Flame-retardant cellulose triacetate articles. Can. pat. 834,626(Feb. 17, 1970); ABIPC 41:A576.

Articles made of CTA are rendered flame retardant by incl. in the CTA cpn. at least 5% of a bromoalkyl phosphate, such as tris(2,3-dibromopropyl) phosphate and a minor amt. of another additive such as an aryl phosphate (e.g., o-phenylphenyl bisphenyl phosphate).

286. Di Pietro, J.; Brinegar, W. C. Flame-retardant cellulose acetate articles. U.S. pat. 3,597,242(Aug. 3, 1971); ABIPC 42:A7126.

Flame-retardant films and filaments are formed from a CDA soln. which also contains a halogenated paraffin and a synergistic agent such as triphenyl phosphate.

287. Eulgem, A.; Woinke, R.; Mummert, G. Mixtures for the manufacture of molded bodies of cellulose acetate and cellulose nitrate. Ger. pat. 1,254,345 (Exam. copy Nov. 16, 1967); ABIPC 40:A4041.

The thermoplastic molding cpns. claimed in this pat. are similar to those provided in Fr. pat. 1,353,374; see Abstr. No. 292.

288. Faraone, G.; Giorgetti, A. Cellulose acetate solutions and the manufacture of self-sustaining films therefrom. U.S. pat. 3,291,625(Dec. 13, 1966); ABIPC 37:A9154.

A method of forming a self-sustaining film of low flammability comprises forming a methylene chloride soln. of CA having an acetyl content of 42.5-44.0% and 5-25 parts by wt. of sucrose octadiphenyl phosphate per 100 parts of CA, casting a film of the soln. on a solid substrate, and stripping the film from the substrate.

289. Harrington, R. C., Jr.; Bond, J. H. Fire-resistant cellulose ester compositions. U.S. pat. 3,437,497(April 8, 1969); ABIPC 40:A1327.

Cellulose esters such as CA are rendered flame-resistant by trmt. with a cpn. obtained by reacting a cpd. having the formula $P(sub n)N(sub n-1)Cl(sub 2n + 3)$ where n is an integer greater than 1 with a pentahalogenated phenol with or without further reaction with ammonia.

290. McClure, R. L. Flame-retardant cellulosic compositions. Can. pat. 839,803(April 21, 1970); ABIPC 41:A4591.

Cellulosic films and filaments having flame-retardant props. are formed by adding to the cellulosic soln. used a vinyl chloride polymer and Sb oxide.

291. Pohlemann, H.; Wurmb, R.; Braun, P. Process for the manufacture of flame-resistant regenerated cellulose material. Ger. pat. 1,906,381(Sept. 3, 1970); ABIPC 42:A4069.

RC film is rendered flameproof through incorporation in the nonregenerated cellulose soln. of cpds. obtained by reacting alcs. or phenols (EtOH, BuOH, cyclohexanol, phenol, pentachlorophenol) with phosphonitrile chloride.

292. Rheinische Gummi- und Celluloidfabrik. Process for the manufacture of a synthetic material based on cellulose acetate. Fr. pat. 1,353,374(Jan. 13, 1964); ABIPC 36:A6094.

A thermoplastic matl., which has the desirable props. of celluloid, but is transparent and flame resistant, contains 24-48% CA, 12-36% CN, and 20-40% of a plasticizer, such as a phosphoric acid ester or a mixt. of such esters. The recommended method of prepn. consists in mixing 65-75 parts of a mixt. contg. 65-75% CA and 25-35% of CN, with 25-35 parts of the plasticizer, allowing the cpn. to swell in a solvent such as acetone, mixing and homogenizing, and removing excess solvent by pressing. An agent for stabilizing the cpn. against the action of light can be added. Suitable plasticizers are org. phosphates, halogenated org. phosphates, and phthalic acid esters. For example, trichloroethyl phosphate or its mixt. with dibutyl phthalate can be used.

293. Susuki, R. New type of composite material, ''LR''-PPC [powdered polymer composite]. J. Japan Petr. Inst. 14, no. 2:91-5(1971); Jap.; CA 75:A6774.

Flame-retardation and water resistance of Ca sulfate-filled PE resin, and use of the resin as pkg. matls. were presented with 2 refs.

294. Togiya, J.; Fujita, E.; Suzuki, M.; Tamiya, S. Method of preparation of flameproof plastic material comprising nitrocellulose as the main ingredient. Jap. pat. 6747('51)(Oct. 29, 1951); Engl. transl. available (5 p.); can also be obtained from SLA; ABIPC 36:A4233.

A flameproof plastic matl. is obtained by compounding CN with a chloro-hydric phosphate triester as plasticizer, with or without the use of camphor or other plasticizers. For example, 1140 g. of CN (contg. 35% alc.) is com-pounded with 260 g. chlorohydric phosphate triester and 29 g. of 94% (vol.) alc. to yield a prod. having an ignition point of 182 C.

295. Wood, E. L.; Gibson, R. E. Self-extinguishing cellulose acetate compositions. U.S. pat. 3,515,565(June 2, 1970); ABIPC 41:A6663.

CA is plasticized with a mixt. of trialkyl phosphate and an org. Br cpd. such as 2,4,6-tribromophenyl acetate. The prod. has flame-resistant props. of self-extinguishing type.

SYNTHESIS

296. Danilov, S. N.; Kutsenko, L. I.; Kiselev, A. D. Method of obtaining flame-resistant cellulose esters. USSR pat. 216,251(Filed Feb. 26, 1966); Izobret no. 14:93(1968); Russ.; ABIPC 39:A3124.

Cellulosic matls. are flameproofed by introducing into the cellulose mols. both P and N simult. The matls. are reacted at 20-60 C., in an org. solvent medium, with isocyanates of dialkyl- or diarylphosphoric or -phosphinic acid.

297. Fuzesi, S.; Lapkin, M. Phosphorus-containing starch oxyalkylated polyethers and their preparation. U.S. pat. 3,399,190(Aug. 27, 1968); ABIPC 39:A6804.

A process of prepg. P-contg. starch-based polyethers comprises mixing starch with concd. phosphoric acid at an elevated temp. to hydrolyze the starch to glucose, and oxyalkylating the resultant mixt. A polyhydric alc. may also be admixed with the hydrolyzed starch prior to oxyalkylation. The prod. is useful in the prepn. of PU foams having flame-retardant props.

298. Howard, E. G., Jr. Selected sulfur derivatives of pentachlorobutadiene and the synthesis thereof. U.S. pat. 3,214,464(Oct. 26, 1965); ABIPC 37:A1377.

Pentachloro-1,3-butadienyl derivs., incl. sulfenyl halides, sulfonyl halides, sulfonamides, and alkyl thioethers, are provided for use in flame-proofing paper.

299. Knoth, W. H. Boron compounds and their preparation. Brit. pat. 956,394(April 29, 1964); ABIPC 35:A4692.

The B cpds. provided are of the formula $M_a[B_{10}H_{10-y}X_y]_b$, where M is an atom or group of atoms which forms a cation, X is a monovalent substituent capable of replacing H in a benzene nucleus (such as a halogen), y is a positive whole number from 1 to 10 inclusive, and a and b are 1, 2, or 3, the values being such that a multiplied by the valence of M is equal to 2b. Where the cpds. are highly halogenated, e.g., salts of $B_{10}Br_{10}$ anion, they are useful as impregnating agents for retarding the combustion of cellulosic prods. such as paper. In an example, ammonium $B_{10}Br_{10}$ is used for this purpose.

300. Kutsenko, L. I.; Kiselev, A. D.; Ryabokon', L. D.; Danilov, S. N. Synthesis of cellulose dimethyl phosphonocarbamate. (Phosphorylated derivatives of cellulose. Part 5.) Zh. Prikl. Khim. 40, no. 10:2303-8(Oct., 1967); Russ.; ABIPC 39:A4579.

In the previous publn. the synt. of cellulose dialkylphosphinates has been reported. On the assumption that the introduction into cellulose of urethan groups bound to P would increase its flame resistance, as well as impart to cellulose certain desirable props., such as soly. in many solvents and the capacity to form films and threads, cellulosic matls. (bleached cotton linters, wood sulfite pulp, and RC) were reacted with the dimethyl ester of isocyanatophosphoric acid. Essential conditions for the prepn. of derivs. with a high DS (2-2.7) were the use of a solvent (preferably pyridine or DMSO) and prelim. activation with an amine. The reaction temp. had little effect, and esters with a high DS were obtained at 20 C. Sulfite pulp and RC had the same reaction rate, cotton cellulose reacted more slowly. The optimum molar ratio of isocyanatophosphate was 2.5-3 mole/OH group of glucose unit. Depending on conditions of pptn., the cellulose dimethyl phosphonocarbamates were either a white powder or flakes. They did not ignite when placed in a flame, and, at a DS of 1.5, were sol. in many solvents, incl. water. Transparent films, obtained from the carbamates, had a tensile strength comparable to that of CDA films.

301. Monsanto Co. Halogen-containing organic di-phosphate derivatives and compositions containing them. Brit. pat. 1,033,252(June 22, 1966); ABIPC 38:A388.

The cpds. of the present invention are of use in flameproofing pulp and paper, as well as in modifying the props. of a wide variety of other matls. The cpds. claimed are prepd. by reacting the pentaerythritol ester of phos-phorochloridous or phosphorobromidous acid with Cl or Br, then reacting the prod. with an epoxide such as ethylene oxide. A typical final prod. is 2,2-bis(chloro-methyl)-1,3-propylenebis[bis(2)-(chloroethyl)phosphate].

302. Muratova, U. M.; Askarov, M. A.; Yuldashev, A. Synthesis of chloro-
derivatives of cellulose with the purpose of subsequent phosphorylation. Khim.
i Fiz.-Khim. Prirodn. i Sintetich. Polimerov, Akad. Nauk Uz. SSR, Inst. Khim.
Polimerov no. 2:153-5(1964); Russ.; ABIPC 35:A5308.

The use of chloro-derivs. for cellulose phosphorylation (e.g., for the
purpose of flameproofing) is based on the conversion of trivalent P acid esters
into pentavalent P acid esters under the influence of Cl-contg. cpds. The
chloro-derivs. of cellulose were obtained by reacting cotton linters with
thionyl chloride (I) in the presence of pyridine. The content of Cl in chlorinated
cellulose depended on the concn. of (I), the temp., and the time of the reaction.
At a temp. of 60 C., and a reaction time of 4 hr., the Cl content was 0.84, 2.49,
and 7.85% at 0.73, 11.6, and 36.5 g. (I)/g. cellulose, resp. At 11.6 g. (I)/g.
cellulose, and a temp. of 97 C., the Cl content was 3.39 and 5.15%, for reaction
times of 2 and 4 hr., resp.

303. Muratova, U. M.; Yuldashev, A. Preparation of phosphorus derivatives
of cellulose in the reaction of tosyl esters with trialkyl phosphites and sodium
dialkyl phosphites. Vysokomol. Soed. 10B, no. 8:594-8(Aug., 1968); Russ.; ABIPC
40:A7642.

The synt. of P derivs. of cellulose contg. the C-P bond, has been described
in an earlier publ., using chlorodeoxycellulose as the starting matl. Similar
derivs. were now obtained by reacting cellulose tosylates with the phosphites.
During the reaction, there is isomerization of trivalent P into pentavalent P
with formation of C-P bonds. In the reaction with triethyl phosphite, a max.
content of P of 4.21% was obtained at 160-165 C. and a ratio of cellulose tosylate
to the phosphite of 1:5. Simult. with substitution of the tosyl groups, there was
their sapon., so that the no. of tosyl groups removed was greater than the no.
of P-contg. groups introduced. The derivs. contained, however, substantial amts.
of S (4.96% at a P content of 4.21%, and an initial DS of cellulose tosylate of
114). In the reaction of cellulose tosylate with Na dimethyl and Na diethyl
phosphites, there was a nearly complete removal of S when proper conditions were
used (82-85 C., a molar ratio 1:10, a medium of tetrahydrofuran/DMF mixt.). The
max. P introduced was 10.87%. The P derivs. of cellulose are flame resistant at
a P content of 2%, and are resistant to hydrolysis.

304. Muratova, U. M.; Yuldashev, A. Reaction of chlorodeoxycellulose with
sodium dialkyl phosphites. Vysokomol. Soed. 10B, no. 3:163-6(March, 1968); Russ.;
ABIPC 39:A9341.

Phosphorylated cellulose derivs., with the P atom linked directly to the C
atom of cellulose, were obtained by reacting chlorodeoxycellulose with Na dimethyl
and Na diethyl phosphites. The P content of the derivs. depended on the conditions
of the reaction. It increased with the amt. of the phosphites and the Cl content
of cellulose. The derivs., which can be called dialkyl esters of cellulose-
phosphinic acid, either retained the structure of the initial chlorocellulose,
or, if they dissolved in the reaction medium and were pptd., were obtained in
the form of powders. They were flame resistant. The max. DS, in gamma units,
was 24. The reaction rate was higher with dimethyl than with diethyl phosphite.

305. Nachbur, H.; Maeder, A. Phosphorus-containing reaction products.
Can. pat. 838,139(March 31, 1970); ABIPC 41:A3484.

A condensation prod. derived from a 1,3,5-triazine and certain P cpds. particularly phosphonopropionic acid amides is reacted with HCHO and, optionally, a 1-4 C alkanol to form a prod. of use in flameproofing cellulosic textiles. For example, the condensation prod. can be derived from 3-dimethyl-phosphonopropion-amide and hexamethylolmelamine.

306. Nachbur, H.; Maeder, A.; Starck, B. P. Phosphorus-containing reaction products, processes for their production and their application. Brit. pat. 1,197,591(July 8, 1970); ABIPC 41:A8636.

Paper and textiles are flameproofed with a P-contg. prod. obtained by reacting certain P-contg. cpds. with glyoxal, HCHO, and, optionally, urea and an alkanol or alkenol. Such a cpd. is obtained by reacting 3-(dimethyl-phosphono)propionamide with glyoxal and HCHO.

307. Olin Mathieson Chemical Corp. Chlorinated polyhydroxy polyethers and polyurethane foams prepared therefrom. Brit. pat. 1,186,537(April 2, 1970); ABIPC 41:A5535.

Starch or other carbohydrate is reacted with 4,4,4-trichloro-1,2-epoxybutane in the presence of an acid catalyst at 20-300 C. The prod. is of use as an intermediate in the prepn. of flame-retardant PU cpns., of use in foams, pkg. matls., adhesives, coatings, etc.

308. Polyakov, A. I.; Smagin, V. V.; Il'ina, L. A. Method of obtaining nonflammable cellulose derivatives. USSR pat. 246,499(Filed June 26, 1967); Publ. Otkryt. Izobret. no. 21:21(1969); ABIPC 40:A6982.

Cellulosic matls. are trd. with phosphorylating agents at elevated temp. Specifically, the cellulosic matls. are vinyl ethers of cellulose, and the phosphorylating agents are cpds. of the gen. formula $HX-P:Y(R)_2$, where X is S, chloral, or an oxymethylene, oxyethylene, or thioethylene group: Y is O or S, and R is a OMe, OEt, or OPr group. The cellulose derivs. are trd. at a temp. of 40-150 C.

309. Predvoditelev, D. A.; Buyanova, V. K.; Konkin, A. A. Method of obtaining flame-resistant polyols. USSR pat. 242,160(Filed Feb. 13, 1968); Publ. Otkryt. Izobret. no. 15:23(1969); ABIPC 40:A4968.

To synthesize polymeric polyols contg. in their mols. chem. bound Sb atoms, the initial polyol, such as cellulose, PV alc., or PF resin, is reacted with an Sb acid chloride of the gen. formula $SbCl_x(OR)_{3-x}$, where R is an alkyl, and x is a whole no. equal to 1, 2, or 3. The reaction is carried out with heating with or without a solvent, in the presence of a nitrogenous base.

310. Predvoditelev, D. A.; Nifant'ev, E. E.; Rogovin, Z. A. Structure and properties of cellulose and its derivatives. 174. Synthesis of esters of cellulose with hypophosphorous [phosphonous] acid. Vysokomol. Soed. 7, no. 5:791-4(May, 1965); Russ.; ABIPC 36:A3126.

The synt. of cellulose phosphonites (the last of the series of esters of trivalent P acids) is reported. The reaction was carried out by the method, recently devd. for low-mol. aliphatic alcs. [cf. Zh. Obshchei Khim. 35:758 (1965)], which consists in reacting the alc. directly with phosphonous acid. Two procedures were used, viz., heating cellulose with a soln. of the acid in an org. solvent, and heating cellulose with a small amt. of acid, adsorbed on the fibers, in an atm. of Ar. Only the second procedure gave satisfactory results, yielding esters with a P content of up to 14%, corresp. to a DS of 0.95. The esters were easily hydrolyzed, their resistance to water being of a lower order than that of cellulose phosphites. Addnl. expts., in which cellulose was reacted with ammonium phosphonite, indicated that the latter is a less active esterifying agent. The esters contained up to 5.88% P, and also contained N (evidently because of the side reaction of esterification with phosphorous acid). At a content of P of 2.65%, the cellulose esters contg. N, were flame resistant. The esters contg. N were more resistant to hydrolysis than esters obtained in the reaction with phosphonous acid.

311. Predvoditelev, D. A.; Tyuganova, M. A.; Nifant'ev, E. E.; Rogovin, Z. A. The structure and properties of cellulose and its derivatives. 164. Synthesis of cellulose phosphites by transesterification with dimethyl phosphite and their chemical conversions. Zh. Prikl. Khim. 40, no. 1:171-7(Jan., 1967); Russ.; ABIPC 38:A2578.

The transesterification reaction between cellulose and dimethyl phosphite at 120-180 C. took place at the same rate in the presence and in the absence of the catalyst (NaOH). In the presence of an excess phosphite, first mixed esters were formed, then, upon prolonged reaction, an almost complete replacement of the Me groups took place. The max. gamma of cellulose phosphites was 128. Compared with other phosphites, the reaction rate with dimethyl phosphite was higher, evidently because of the small size of the alkyl radical. Similarly to other esters of cellulose and trivalent P acids, the phosphites underwent hydrolysis easily. Their resistance to hydrolysis could be substantially increased by converting them into derivs. of pentavalent P. Thus, hydroxy-methylphosphonate of cellulose (obtained by reaction with HCHO in alk. medium), and cellulose phosphates and amidophosphates (obtained by oxidn. with N oxides) were quite resistant to hydrolysis. Detns. of the flame resistance of the cpds. obtained confirmed the previously reached conclusion that flame resistance depends not only on the amt. of P introduced, but also on the structure of the P acid residue. Large alkyl radicals and the presence of P-N bond tend to reduce flame resistance.

312. Rogovin, Z. A.; Tyuganova, M. A.; Gabrielyan, G. A.; Konnova, N. F. Preparation of non-flammable viscose rayon and polyacrylonitrile fibers. Khim. Volokna no. 3:27-30(1966); Russ.; Transl. in Engl. (9 p.) available from IPC at copying cost; ABIPC 38:A7369.

The starting matls. for the prepn. of nonflammable fibers were dialdehyde cellulose and modified PAN contg. aldehyde groups. Both were reacted with dimethyl phosphite in the absence of catalysts or in the presence of an alk. catalyst [NaOH, ammonia (I)]. In the presence of (I) complete nonflammability of cellulose was achieved at lower P content than in the presence of NaOH or in the absence of catalysts. In the presence of (I), two parallel reactions take place, viz., transesterification with the formation of cellulose phosphite, and the reaction of dimethyl phosphite with the aldehyde groups with the

formation of a cellulose amino phosphonate. The prods. of the two reactions
can be sepd. as aminophosphonic acid derivs. are resistant to hydrolysis, while
cellulose phosphites are easily hydrolyzed; when the reaction with dimethyl
phosphite is carried out at 80 C., the phosphites formed are fully hydrolyzed
upon boiling. In prods. obtained at 100 C., a considerable amt. of P is
retained flg. 3 hr. boiling. In the case of PAN, the fibers become nonflammable
at a P content of 3.5%, but to obtain a nonhydrolyzable prod., the reaction
must be carried out in the presence of amines.

313. Yuldashev, A.; Abidov, S. R.; Askarov, M. A. Preparation of flame-
resistant cellulose by treatment with phosphorus-containing polyesters. Dokl.
Akad. Nauk Uz. SSR 25, no. 9:30-1(1968); Russ.; ABIPC 42:A6649.

Flame-resistant cellulosic matls. were obtained by impregnation with unsatd.
P-contg. linear polyesters in the presence of polymn. initiators, such as benzoyl
peroxide. The polyesters were obtained by condensation of vinylphosphonic
acid dichloride with hydroxy cpds., and by homocondensation of beta,beta'-
dichloroethyl ester of vinylphosphinic acid. The method involves no formation
of intermediate cpd. and does not affect the mech. strength of the cellulosic
matls. The trd. matls. remain flame resistant after washing with soap soln.

314. Yuldashev, A.; Askarov, M. A.; Sadykov, M. M. Modification of cotton
cellulose properties with certain organic phosphorus compounds. Uzbek. Khim.
Zh. 11, no. 3:44-5(1967); Russ.; ABIPC 38:A9041.

In continuing the study of cellulose modification through the reaction with
chlorides of P acids, samples of cellulose, of cellulose oxidized with periodate,
and of reduced periodate cellulose, were reacted in benzene in the presence of
pyridine, at 80-85 C., with mono- and dichlorides of phenyl-, o-chlorophenyl-,
and p-chlorophenylphosphoric acid. The reaction prods. were studied by IR
spectroscopy. All spectra contained an absorption band at 1250 cm. exp(-1),
charac. of the P = O bond. The modified celluloses contained up to 5.32% P,
and at P contents of over 1%, were flame-resistant.

315. Yuldashev, A.; Perlina, R. V.; Sadykov, M. M.; Usmanov, K. U. Phosphorylation of modified cellulose preparations with phosphoric acid chlorides.
Vysokomol. Soed. 8, no. 2:231-4(Feb., 1966); Russ.; ABIPC 37:A1851.

Cotton linters cellulose, cellulose oxidized with periodate to contain
a small amt. of aldehyde groups at carbons 2 and 3, and cellulose contg. primary
OH groups at carbons 2 and 3 (obtained by Na borohydride redn. of periodate-
oxidized prepn.), were phosphorylated with dichlorides of phenylphosphoric and
o-chlorophenylphosphoric acids. The reaction was carried out in a mixt. of
benzene and pyridine at a cellulose:acid chloride ratio of 1:3, for 30 min.
at 75-80 C. The reactivity of the cellulose prepns. was evald. from the amt.
of P introduced into the macromols. The phosphorylation prod. of nonmodified
cellulose contained 2.56% P, the phosphorylation prod. of oxidized cellulose
contained 0.81% P, and that of reduced cellulose 5.32% P. An increase in the
content of aldehyde groups from 2 to 4.3% in oxidized cellulose had no effect
on the phosphorylation process, the amt. of P bound remaining the same, and
much lower than in the case of nonmodified cellulose. The course of the reaction
was similar with the two phosphoric acid chlorides. Because of its higher content

of P, phosphorylated reduced cellulose had a higher degree of flame resistance than the phosphorylated nonmodified cellulose. The probable mechanism of the reaction of modified cellulose with the acid chlorides is discussed.

316. Yuldashev, A.; Muratova, U. M.; Askarov, M. A. Phosphorylation of cotton cellulose with some phosphorous acid esters via chlorocellulose. Vysokomol. Soed. 7, no. 11:1923-6(Nov., 1965); Russ.; ABIPC 36:A7772.

The Arbuzov reaction was carried out with di- and trialkyl phosphites and chlorocellulose (instead of cellulose chloroacetate, as reported in the lit.). Chlorocellulose was synthesized by reacting cotton cellulose with thionyl chloride in an org. base medium. IR spectroscopy of the prods. indicated that with both the di- and trialkyl phosphites, the P atom was linked directly to the C atom of cellulose. The presence of absorption at 1259 cm. exp(-1), characteristic of the P = O bond, indicated that the Arbuzov rearrangement took place in both cases. The P content of phosphorylated cellulose depended on the conditions of the reaction (temp., time), but was affected little by the Cl content of the initial chlorocellulose. The rate of the reaction was higher with the dialkyl than with the trialkyl phosphites, and increased with decreasing size of the alkyl radical (Me, Et, and Pr esters were used). The phosphorylated celluloses had bactericidal props. and were flame resistant.

317. Yuldashev, A.; Sadykov, M. M.; Sadovnikova, V. I.; Ziyavutdinov, K. M. Strength retention of cellulose phosphorylated with phosphorus oxychlorides. Uzbek. Khim. Zh. 13, no. 4:76-7(1969); Russ.; ABIPC 41:A7128.

In order to obtain flameproofed fibers and fabrics which have ion exchange props., cellulose is usually phosphorylated. The HCl liberated by the use of P oxychlorides as the phosphorylating reagent causes extensive degradation. Therefore, to avoid this problem, it was suggested that P oxychlorides be used with low-substituted cyanoethylated cellulose, which is more resistant to the action of acids and higher temps. The reaction was carried out in a mixt. of benzene and pyridine using a bath ratio of 1:40. Studies in which methyl phosphonic dichloride was used as the phosphorylating agent showed that as the molar concn. of the reagent and the reaction time and temp. increased, the P content in the prod. also increased, and that a prod. with a P content of 2% was highly flame resistant. A study of the phys. and mech. props. of the prods. showed that the cyanoethylated cellulose fabrics had a tensile strength loss of only 10-15% after phosphorylation, while fabrics which were not cyanoethylated showed a loss of 35-40%.

318. Yuldashev, A.; Tsveshko, G. S. Preparation of phosphorus-containing derivatives of cellulose. Dokl. Akad. Nauk Uz. SSR no. 5:32-4(1965); Russ.; ABIPC 39:A7376.

The derivs. were obtained by reacting cotton cellulose with dichlorides of P acids, incl. dichlorides of o-chlorophenylphosphoric, beta-chloroethyl-phosphinic acid, and vinylphosphinic acid. The cellulose (through dehydro-chlorination or directly) can be used for further synt. through mercuration, thiocyanation, or epoxidation. In addn. these two acid chlorides yield C-P bonds, thus enhancing the flame resistance of modified cellulose. To prevent degradation of cellulose during the reaction, the HCl formed is bound by suitable acceptors, and to assure uniform distribution of the substituents, the reaction is carried out in solvents. The derivs. obtained contained 0.92-5.42% P.

319. Zharova, T. Y.; Tyuganova, M. A.; Levin, B. B.; Smirnova, E. A.; Rogovin, Z. A. The structure and properties of cellulose and its derivatives. (232) Synthesis of derivatives of cellulose and alpha-phenylvinylphosphonic acid. Vysokomol. Soed. 9, Ser. A, no. 3:698-703(March, 1967); Russ.; ABIPC 38:A5109.

Reaction of cellulose contg. a small amt. of aromatic amino groups with alpha-phenylvinylphosphonic acid (I) gave prods. the P content of which did not exceed 0.8%. Attempts to use a redox system (Bridgeport method), or cellulose contg. peroxide groups, gave neg. results. Copolymers of cellulose and (I) were successfully synthesized, however, when the aromatic amino groups in cellulose were diazotized. In this case graft copolymerization was initiated by free macroradicals formed when the diazonium salt was decomposed in the presence of metal salts (Fe, Cu). Simult. a side reaction took place, i.e., the reaction of diazonium salt with (I), the prod. being a cellulose ether. The last reaction predominated in an atm. of air, while copolymerization occurred chiefly in an atm. of an inert gas. Graft copolymers of cellulose with poly-(I) were flame resistant at a P content of over 3.6%.

320. Zhbankov, R. G.; Marupov, R.; Balabaeva, M. D.; Tsyuganova, M. A.; Lishevskaya, M. A. Study of new, technically valuable, cellulose derivatives by infrared spectroscopy. Vestsi. Akad. Navuk Belarus. SSR, Ser. Fiz.-Tekh. Navuk no. 2:38-41(1963); Beloruss.; ABIPC 35:A7867.

New types of cellulose derivs. having useful props. (flame resistance, creaseproofness, ion-exchange capacity, bactericidal action, etc.) have been synthesized recently at the Moscow Textile Research Inst. The authors studied the structure of some of these derivs. by IR spectroscopy. Absorption spectra are presented and interpreted for the flg. cpds.: cellulose methylphosphonates with various P contents; cellulosic ion-exchangers contg. substituted benzene-sulfonic acid groups; derivs. obtained by reacting cellulose with chloroalkane acids; and stable cellulose methylxanthates.

TESTING

321. Basch, A.; Wasserman, T. Determination of phosphorus in cellulosic fabrics. Textile Res. J. 40, no. 7:676(July, 1970); ABIPC 42:A6651.

A description is given of a procedure for detg. the P in cellulosic fabrics trd. with flame retardant P cpds. It consists mainly of digesting the sample with a mineral acid, measuring the absorbance of the soln., and detg. the P concn. from a calibration curve.

322. Carey, J. P.; TAPPI-ASTM Joint Paper Testing Committee. Flame resistance of treated paper and paperboard. (Proposed revision of T461 m-48 as a tentative standard.) Tappi 50, no. 8:169A(Aug., 1967); ABIPC 38:A3267.

This method is applicable to all flameproofed papers and boards up to 1.5 mm. (0.06 in.) thick. It is related to ASTM D777. The main change in the revision is the requirement of a metal cabinet to enclose the test sample. In gen., papers that show an av. char length of over 11.5 cm. or of which any specimen has a char length beyond 15.0 cm. are not considered flame-resistant.

323. Carroll-Porczynski, C. Z. Fabric flammability. New testing methods and equipment. Text. Inst. Ind. 9, no. 7:188-94(1971); CA 75:A141821.

DTA, thermogravimetric anal., mass spectroscopy, and scanning electron microscopy were used to study the fire resistance of fabrics made of synthetic and natural fibers. The smoke emission during fire, the toxicol. of flammable textiles, and O depletion effect on toxicity are discussed.

324. Hay, P. M. Flame-retardant cellulose: a new method of evaluation. Am. Dyestuff Reptr. 53, no. 19:23-6(Sept. 14, 1964); ABIPC 35:A4314.

Two cotton fabrics, an 80 x 80 cotton and an 8-oz. cotton twill, and cellophane were used to det. the influence of the phys. structure of cellulose on the effectiveness of flame retardants, and to develop a sensitive test for evalg. fire retardants. It appears that more compact forms of cellulose, i.e., the 8-oz. cotton twill and cellophane, are better suited for testing the efficiency of flame retardants. The 80 x 80 cotton, being lighter and less compact, requires more flame retardant to reduce flammability and is more subject to variation in testing. A new burning test method, which uses small quarter-ellipse specimens, was found to be applicable to testing both cellophane and fabric. The new test is more useful for research purposes than the std. vert. flame test (AATCC 34-1952) [American Association of Textile Chemists and Colorists] in that a broader range of flammability can be quantitatively detd. An inverse relationship was found between the P content of the 8-oz. twill or cellophane and the flammability.

325. Hofmann, P.; Rohringer, P. Burning behavior of textiles. Textilveredlung 6, no. 10:664-71(1971); Ger.; CA 76:A26262.

326. Janku, M. Identification of the maximum non-flammability point of cellulosic textiles treated with the ''antimony-chlorine'' flame retardant. Textil 26, no. 2:54-8, 65(1971); Czech.; ABIPC 42:A4594.

Samples of cotton fabric were trd. with a flame retardant consisting of a soln. of chlorinated PVC and chlorinated paraffin in trichloroethylene contg. dispersed antimony trioxide. The wt. ratio of antimony trioxide/active Cl in the flame retardant ranged from 0.1 to 10. The trd. samples were subjected to pyrolysis in presence of air and the gaseous prods. were anald. by gas chromat. to det. the C monoxide/C dioxide ratio in the gases. It was observed that the samples which yielded gases contg. C monoxide and C dioxide in a ratio ranging from 0.162 to 0.225, corresp. to the Sb/Cl ratio of 0.416-2.291 in the flame retardant used, were flameproof. It was concluded that neither Cl nor Sb alone were efficient in redg. the flammability of textiles. The optimal effect was obtained with the flame retardant contg. Sb and Cl in a wt. ratio of 1.12. Pyrolysis of a cotton fabric sample trd. with this retardant yielded gases in which the C monoxide/C dioxide ratio was approx. 0.5.

327. Kacafirek, S.; Kaspar, Z. Papers with reduced flammability. Papir Celuloza 26, no. 4:77-8, 82(1971); Czech.; ABIPC 42:A4764.

Various std. methods for the detn. of the flammability of papers and boards are revd. It is concluded that the most suitable is the TAPPI std. method T 461 os-48. Samples of kraft paper were trd. with inorg. salts (Ca and Mg chlorides and borax) and with the Schimmer & Schwarz, the Flacavon R-PS, and the Vi-tard (PVdC and Sb chloride) flame retardants. With 16% (based on the wt. of paper) of Ca or Mg chloride, 47% of the Schimmer & Schwarz agent contg. a special size, or 35% of Vi-tard the papers obtained were nonflammable, when tested by the TAPPI method. The samples trd. with Ca and Mg chlorides were hygroscopic, and the salts as well as the Schimmer & Schwarz agent could be washed out with water.

328. Lipska, A. E. Effect of flame retardants on thermal degradation of alpha-cellulose in nitrogen. Stanford Res. Inst. Project PYU-8150, Ann. Report, Aug., 1970:42 p.; Avail. from NTIS, AD 715411; ABIPC 42:A4568.

Measurements for use in assessing the Parker-Lipska model for the decpn. of cellulose (cf. ABIPC 41:A1978) are reported. These include changes in mol.wt. during isothermal pyrolysis and increases in char yield and wt.-loss rate due to retardant trmt. These expts. also investigated the role of 1,5-anhydro-2,3-deoxy-beta-D-pent-2-eno-furanose (a major prod. of thermally degraded cellulose and levoglucosan) in the char formation process of fire-retardant trd. cellulose. The isolated furanose deriv., both in the neat form and in the presence of ammonium dihydrogen phosphate, was pyrolyzed and its degradation prods. were anald. by gas chromat. At 276 C., initial pyrolysis of alpha-cellulose results in an abrupt decrease in av. mol.wt. and is fld. by a linear decrease over a prolonged period of heating. Increased yields of char and rates of degradation due to the basic and neut. retardants were in quant. agreement with the predictions of the Parker-Lipska model for decpn. of cellulose. The effects of the acidic retardants, however, were not in agreement with the prediction. These results suggest that some modifications of the model are in order. The results of the pyrolysis expts. on the furanose deriv. support the contention that the excess yield of char in retardant-trd. cellulose is due to the degradation of secondary prods. of cellulose decpn. rather than of the cellulose mol. itself.

329. Lipska, A. E.; Parker, W. J. Kinetics of the pyrolysis of cellulose in the temperature range of 250-300 C. J. Appl. Polymer Sci. 10, no. 10:1439-53 (Oct., 1966); ABIPC 37:A8811.

Alpha-cellulose contg. 0.11-0.14% ash was subjected to isothermal pyrolysis in a double fluidized bath under N in the temp. range 250-300 C. The results are reported in terms of volatilization (based on wt.-loss measurements) and decpn. (in terms of glucosan loss). The findings show 3 distinct stages of pyrolysis at each temp.: an initial period of rapid decpn. and wt. loss; a range in which both the volatilization and decpn. are zero-order; and a region in which the volatilization follows a first-order rate, leaving a char deposit which does not undergo further pyrolysis. The transition between the zero- and first-order behavior occurs at a greater degree of pyrolysis as the temp. is increased. At 288 C., the initial volatilization leaves about 94% of the original wt. and the zero-to-first-order transition occurs at about the point where 50% of the original wt. remains. The residual char is approx. 16% between 276 and 300 C. and is substantially greater at lower temps. The initial wt. loss is due to the decpn. of cellulose rather than simply a loss of adsorbed water. The activation energy for the decpn. and volatilization is 42 kcal./mole for the 250-300 C. range.

330. Lipska, A. E.; Wodley, F. A. Isothermal pyrolysis of cellulose: kinetics and gas chromatographic mass spectrometric analysis of the degradation products. J. Appl. Polymer Sci. 13, no. 5:851-65(May, 1969); ABIPC 40:A7636.

Untrd. and fire retardant-trd. alpha-cellulose was subjected to isothermal pyrolysis in a fluidized bath under N in the temp. range 298-360 C. The results are reported in terms of volatilization (based on wt.-loss measurements) and degradation prods. (based on gas chromat.-mass spectrometric anal.). Wt. loss measurements of cellulose pyrolyzed at 315, 335, and 350 C. revealed 3 distinct phases of pyrolysis which correlated with those previously reported for the temp. range 250-300 C. (see preceding abstr.). The activation energy for decpn. is 42 kcal./mole for the 276-360 C. range. There is little difference in either the quality or rel. quantity of volatiles generated during the 3 different phases of pyrolysis. The fire retardant, K bicarbonate, does not markedly change the types of degradation prods. having mol.wts. below ca. 110, although it does change their rel. concns. The initial rapid wt. loss in both trd. and untrd. samples is not due to desorption of water, but rather, to decpn. of the cellulose mols.

331. Miller, B.; Meiser, C. H., Jr. Measuring the burning rates of fabrics. Text. Chem. Color 3, no. 5:118-22(1971); CA 75:A22275.

The burning rates of cotton, polyester, and nylon textiles are detd. with good precision with an app. in which the textile sample is mounted on a wheel and ignited and the wheel is rotated to keep the flame in a fixed position, i.e., horizontal, upward, or downward burning is accomplished by keeping the flame at the top or sides of the wheel. The burning rates are inversely proportional to fabric wt. but do not correlate with d. The burning rate and the atm. O concn. were linearly related, giving a quant. detn. of relative hazard under O depletion conditions.

332. Millett, M. A.; Western, L. J.; Booth, J. J. Accelerated aging of cellulosic materials: design and application of a heating chamber. Tappi 50, no. 11:74-80A(Nov., 1967); ABIPC 38:A6489.

Construction details and operating characs. are given for an easily fabricated heating chamber of 3-1/4 cu.ft. internal capacity capable of plus or minus 0.1 C. control over the temp. range of 50-200 C. Experience with 6 of these units has shown them to be highly dependable and well suited to the study of the accelerated aging of cellulosic matls. as a chem. rate process. In one appln. of the equipment, the effect of a boric acid-borate fire-retardant trmt. on the aging characs. of an acoustical fiberboard was evald. Both loss in wt. and decrease in modulus of rupture in bending were found to exhibit first-order relationships with time exposed, the trd. board showing the lower rate of prop. loss. Arrhenius plots of half-life data for temps. of 130, 150, and 170 C. gave activation energies of 26.9 and 34.1 kcal./mole for the untrd. and trd. fiberboards, resp. In a second appln., the rel. aging characs. of two unbleached kraft papers, one sized (pH 6.2) and the other unsized (pH 8.2), were evald. on the basis of fold, tear, tensile strength, and viscy. data obtained at 110, 140, and 155 C. The activation energy for thermal degradation was rel. const., 25.5-27.5 kcal./mole for the unsized paper and 20-24 kcal./mole for the sized paper, when detd. for any of the four props. tested.

333. Parker, W. J.; Lipska, A. E. Proposed model for the decomposition of cellulose and the effect of flame retardants. Combustion Inst., Western States Sect. Paper WSS/CI No. 69-25:47 p.(1969); ABIPC 41:A1978.

A model for the decpn. of cellulose is proposed, based on lit. data and supported by lab. tests, and the effect of flame retardants was studied with respect to this model. At temps. above 275 C. the cellulose decpd. through the simult. unzipping of all the cellulose mols., giving a const. rate of decpn. over the pyrolysis period. The unzipping is the only controlling reaction. The rate of decpn. was proportional to the no. of mols. present which was const. over most of the decpn. period. The mol. length decreased linearly with time. After the oxygen links between the glucosan units were broken during the unzipping process, the units were transformed into levoglucosan or participated in the char-forming process with the release of water, carbon dioxide, and hydrogen. The other pyrolysis prods. resulted from the decpn. of levoglucosan. The action of flame retardants was to increase the rate of decpn. and the amt. of char produced. The rate was increased by increasing the no. of mols. through the breaking of inter-ring intramol. bonds. Direct action of the flame retardant on the levoglucosan caused an increase in the char produced and a redn. in the flammability of the volatiles released. 27 ref.

334. Perkins, R. M.; Drake, G. L., Jr.; Reeves, W. A. D[ifferential] T[hermal] A[nalysis] and T[hermo] G[ravimetric] A[nalysis] studies of flame-resistant fabrics. J. Appl. Polymer Sci. 10, no. 7:1041-66(July, 1966); ABIPC 37:A3390.

Prelim. thermal studies were made of cotton fabrics made flame resistant by chem. modification or by blending with a synt. flame-resistant fiber. Differential thermal and thermogravimetric analyses were made in both N and O atmospheres. Differences were found in the thermograms of untrd. control fabrics, depending upon the amt. of purification. Fabrics trd. with the flame-resistant formulations had lower decpn. temps. and higher percentages of residue. Decpn. in O was more complete and proceeded at a lower temp. The IR spectra of selected samples, which were partially or completely charred, are presented. These data are related to theories concerning the degradation of flame-resistant cotton fabrics. 33 ref.

335. Smith, J. K.; Rawls, H. R.; Felder, M. S.; Klein, E. Thermochemical investigation of cotton flame retardance. Textile Res. J. 40, no. 3:211-16 (March, 1970); ABIPC 41:A7121.

Differential scanning calorimetry and thermogravimetric anal. curves were obtained for cotton cellulose in the presence of both flame retarding and non-flame retarding cpds. and evald. quant. for enthalpy, activation energy, total wt. loss, and char remaining after pyrolysis. Twenty-three cpds. were evald. With increasing molar add-on, heat liberated from cellulose decreased for cpds. which did not undergo decpn. in the temp. interval in which cellulose decomposes

(200-400 C.), increased for cpds. which decompose appreciably during or preceding this temp. interval, and was not a function of molar add-on for cpds. which did not interact in any way with cellulose. The kinetics of decpn. for these systems indicated that, while the majority of reactions proceeded as a pseudo first-order process, there were several exceptions to the trend. Activation energy decreased with increasing flame retardancy. The addn. to cellulose of any of the cpds. from the first two groups lowered the onset temp. of decpn. and the temp. at which the first major wt. loss began. This temp. decrease approached some limiting value for all the cpds., and varied from cpd. to cpd. In addn., a large increase in remaining char resulted from a small add-on, and this tended to approach a limiting value as add-on increased.

336. Stamm, G. Present state of flammability testing of textiles. 2. Textilveredlung 6, no. 10:656-60(1971); Ger.; CA 76:A26243.

New standards and regulations for the flammability testing of textiles in Switzerland, Germany, United Kingdom, Sweden, U.S.A., and Japan are rev.

337. Syska, A. D. Exploratory investigation of fire-retardant treatments for particle board. U.S. Forest Serv., Res. Note FPL-0201:20 p.(Aug., 1969); ABIPC 40:A5737.

Douglas-fir and aspen flake-type particle boards, made with 15 common fire-retardant chemicals appl. in several ways, were evald. for flammability, mech. strength, and dimensional stability. The most satisfactory fire-retardant was boric acid-disodium octaborate. Fire test props. were adequate. Tensile strength perpendicular to the surface and modulus of elasticity were approx. the same as those of untrd. board. The modulus of rupture was ca. 75% that of untrd. board. Appln. of the fire-retardant in soln. to the wood particles before drying was more efficient than appln. as a dry powder to the particles immediately after resin spraying. In gen., this study showed that the addn. of most of the fire-retardants caused an appreciable decrease in bond strength, apparently by interfering with the proper curing of the resin. Understanding the nature of this interference leads to the presumption that the strength props. of fire-retardant particle boards could be improved by chem. modification of the fire-retardant chemical or, possibly, the binder resin.

338. Weissler, E. P. Laboratory method for testing the flammability of thin laminate sheets. Kunststoffe 55, no. 11:828-32(Nov., 1965); Ger.; ABIPC 36:A8550.

A lab. app. for measuring the flammability of decorative laminates, particle boards, etc., is described which consists essentially of a propane gas flame combustion chamber. Means are provided for carefully controlling the intensity of the flame. Flammability of the test sample is evald. through measurement of the temp. of the chamber exhaust gases as a function of combustion period.

339. Willard, J. J.; Wondra, R. E. Quantitative evaluation of flame retardant cotton finishes by the limiting oxygen index (LOI) technique. Textile Res. J. 40, no. 3:203-10(March, 1970); ABIPC 41:A7153.

The limiting oxygen index (LOI) technique provided a quant. measure of reduced flammability for fabrics over broad ranges of chem. trmt. Several conventional flame-retardant finishes for cellulosics gave linear LOI relations with P content when compared at fixed N-P ratios. Tris(aziridinyl)phosphine oxide was an exception. Precise measurement of the role of N in enhancing the flame-retardant effectiveness was made with this technique. The synergistic interaction of N and P is described. The synergistic effect did not predominate at a specific N-P ratio. Fabric air permeability was a primary factor governing chem. requirements and is probably more important than fabric wt.

340. Wodley, F. A. Pyrolysis products of untreated and flame retardant treated alpha-cellulose and levoglucosan. San Francisco, U.S. Naval Radiol. Defense Lab. [Final Rept. Contract no. DAHC20-67-C-0149] Aug., 1969:43 p. [AD-704145; avail. from CFSTI]; ABIPC 41:A8150.

A typical gas chromatogram of the volatile pyrolysis prods. (mol.wts. less than 150) of untrd. alpha-cellulose contains 39 peaks; however, mass spectral data indicate that at least 59 cpds. are present. Since the initial pyrolysis prods. undergo decpn., both initial and subsequent decpn. prods. are included in the anal. A total of 37 cpds. were identified, 13 of which have not been previously reported. A comparison of the prods. generated at 330-400 C. indicates that the formation of pyrolysis prods. is essentially indep. of temp. In gen., flame retardant trd. samples produce fewer prods. than untrd. samples, although the cpds. that are present are the same. Some trmts., incl. 4% iodination, 6% benzhydrylation, and 4% iodination-5% benzhydrylation yield only 5 prominent cpds. (water, acetic acid, furfural, 5-methyl-2-furfuraldehyde, and an unknown). Flame retardant concn. seems to affect the formation of prods. more than the type of retardant. Comparisons of the chromatograms obtained for untrd. levoglucosan and cellulose indicate that the decpn. of cellulose probably yields levoglucosan which then decomposes to yield the observed pyrolysis prods.

TEXTILES

341. Aenishanslin, R. Flame-retardant finishes for cellulosic fibers. Ciba Rev. no. 4:35-43(1969); CA 72:A122685.

342. Aenishanslin, R. Problems of flameproof finishing of fibrous materials. Melliand Textilber. 49, no. 10:1210-12(Oct., 1968); Ger.; ABIPC 39:A8413.

Flg. an introduction to the gen. problem of flameproofing of textiles, chem. flameproofing trmts. for cellulosic and synt. textiles are outlined. Testing of flame resistance is also briefly considered.

343. Aenishanslin, R.; Bigler, N. A contribution to the theory and practice of flameproofing treatments on cotton. Textilveredlung 3, no. 9:467-74(Sept., 1968); Ger.; ABIPC 39:A8414.

The theory of flameproofing trmts. for cotton is discussed. Studies are presented in which an attempt was made to follow the pyrolysis of cotton through

microscopy. It is pointed out that flameproofing trmts. do not prohibit combustion, but rather change the course of thermal decpn. of cellulose to avoid
the formation of highly flammable pyrolysis prods. The practice of cotton flameproofing is also examd. using an org. P cpd. as an example of a flameproofing
agent.

344. Aenishanslin, R.; Guth, C.; Hofmann, P.; Maeder, A.; Nachbur, H.
New chemical approach to durable flame-retardant cotton fabrics. Textile Res.
J. 39, no. 4:375-81(April, 1969); ABIPC 40:A3728.

Studies show that a no. of N-methylol cpds. of dialkyl phosphonocarboxylic
acid amides are suitable for prodg. durable flame-retardant finishes on cotton
textiles. The finish is appl. by the pad-dry-cure procedure on conventional
equipment. One cpd. was chosen to illus. their performance. The finishes are
fast to washing and dry cleaning. Tensile strength and abrasion resistance of
trd. fabrics are reduced, but are within tolerable limits. Phosphonate finishes
may modify the shade and lightfastness of dyeings and prints. Gen., however,
vat and naphthol dyes in a wide range of shades have shown high stability to such
finishes.

345. Alvares, N. J.; Anderson, T. H. Ignition hardening of cellulosic
materials. U.S., Clearinghouse Fed. Sci. Tech. Inform., AD 663086. Avail.
CFSTI, 34 pp.(1967); Engl.; CA 68:A79454.

The ignition response of blackened alpha-cellulose and cotton cloth, contg.
fire-retardant additives, was compared to the ignition response of these matls.
without additives. This information was obtained by exposing the samples to
various irradiance levels from a calibrated thermal radiation source. Samples
trd. with retardant cpds. which showed the most promise were then isothermally
pyrolyzed, in air, so that comparisons between the pyrolysis rates of the samples
could be obtained. These comparisons yielded further insight into the mechanism
of thermal degradation. Similar ignition response measurements were made with
specimens exposed to ionizing radiation alpha-cellulose samples contg. a mixt.
of boric acid, borax, and monoammonium phosphate could not be ignited by irradiances
of 4.0 cal./sq.cm./sec. or less. Above this value, transient ignition would
occur but flaming would last only until the ignitible gases were exhausted from
the samples. Cotton cloth contg. a polymeric retardant with the designation
THPC + MM was ignition resistant below an irradiance of 7.0 cal./sq.cm./sec.
Comparison of the pyrolysis rates of the retardant-trd. alpha-cellulose and
cotton showed that the retardant mechanism is qualitatively the same. Gamma
radiation results in ignition retardance of cellulose, while irradn. by neutrons
does not.

346. Androsova, M. V. Flameproof finishing of hydroxy-containing textiles.
Deut. Textiltech. 20, no. 5:294-7(1970); Ger.; CA 73:A36415.

The reactions of cellulose and PV alc. with phosphorous acid esters to prep.
textiles having good flame resistance are discussed.

347. Armour, W. B.; Brown, G. H.; Mazzarella, E. D. Process of bonding
nonwoven fabric with chlorinated atactic polypropylene and the bonded fabric. U.S.
pat. 3,316,122(April 25, 1967); ABIPC 38:A2911.

A process of making a nonwoven bonded fabric having softness, strength, and resistance to fire comprises applg. to a fiber web a binding agent consisting of chlorinated atactic PP dispersed in a liquid medium, then removing the liquid medium. The fibers used in forming the base web can be wood pulp fibers, waste paper fibers, cotton, or synthetics.

348. Arseneau, D. F. A differential thermal analysis study of fire retardants in cellulose. Proc. Can. Wood Chem. Symp., 1st., Toronto 1963:155-60; discn.:161-2(publ. 1965); Engl.; CA 64:6879.

A modified differential thermal analysis app. (CA 56, 3703d) was used, in which the reference thermocouple was unpacked, whereas the sample thermocouple was packed with a 5-mg. sample up to, but not incl., the junction. Cellulose (I) trd. with borax or ammonium chloride (II) was compared with untrd. (I). The use of the Kissinger (CA 52, 5104f) graphic method of activation-energy detn. indicated that (II) trmt. increased the activation energy of the endothermic discoloration reaction to 31.4 kcal. from 27.8 kcal. with (I). With borax, the activation energy of this reaction was 25.1 kcal. The major exothermic reaction has an activation energy of 34.5 kcal. with (I), but 40.3 kcal. with borax-impregnated-(I). Borax was found to hinder heat transfer by foam formation.

349. Beninate, J. V.; Boylston, E. K.; Drake, G. L., Jr.; Reeves, W. A. Application of a new phosphonium flame retardant [to textile fabrics]. Am. Dyestuff Reptr. 57, no. 25:P981-5(Dec. 2, 1968); ABIPC 39:A9364.

A new flame retardant based on the reaction prod. of tetrakishydroxy-methylphosphonium chloride and NaOH has been appl. to cotton. The prod., which is weakly basic, is believed to be an equil. mixt. of tetrakishydroxymethyl-phosphonium hydroxide (THPOH) and trishydroxymethylphosphine in water. A typical trmt. consists of padding fabric through a 30% soln. of THPOH, drying the fabric to approx. 10% moisture, and then exposing it to ammonia vapor. The ammonia reacts immediately with the THPOH to form a highly insol. flame resistant polymer inside the fabric. Fabrics trd. by this method showed no change in tensile strength and only minimal losses in tearing strength.

350. Beninate, J. V.; Boylston, E. K.; Drake, G. L., Jr.; Reeves, W. A. Conventional pad/dry/cure process for durable flame and wrinkle resistance with tetrakis(hydroxymethyl)phosphonium hydroxide. Textile Res. J. 38, no. 3:267-72 (March, 1968); ABIPC 39:A5534.

A durable flame-retardant finish is obtained by padding cotton with an aq. soln. of tetrakis(hydroxymethyl)phosphonium hydroxide (THPOH), urea, and tri-methylolmelamine, drying at moderate temp., and curing at elevated temp. Solns. of 25-34% total solids contg. the 3 components (THPOH, urea, trimethylolmelamine) in a molar ratio of 2:4:1 imparted flame resistance with only minimal losses in breaking and tearing strengths. Fabrics trd. by this process possessed wash/wear and permanent press props. as well as flame resistance. Flame resistance was retained after boiling the trd. fabrics in a soap/Na carbonate soln. for 3 hr. or after 15 laundering cycles.

351. Beninate, J. V.; Boylston, E. K.; Drake, G. L., Jr.; Reeves, W. A. Imparting flame resistance to fibrous textiles from an alkaline medium. U.S. pat. 3,607,356(Sept. 21, 1971); CA 76:A15737.

Flame resistance was imparted to cellulose-contg. and wool textiles by impregnating the fabric with a pH 7.5-7.9 aq. soln. contg. 10-40% tris(hydroxymethyl)phosphine (I) to a wet pickup of approx. 70-100%, drying the impregnated textile to approx. 10-20% moisture content, treating (I) with ammonia gas (II) 2-6 min. at room temp. to deposit in and on the textile a polymd. P-contg. substance rel. insol. in common solvents, washing, and drying. Thus, cotton sateen was impregnated by a soln. (pH 7.8), prepd. by mixing a 30% aq. (I) soln. with a soln. contg. NaOH 21, water 152, and an 80% aq. tetrakis(hydroxymethyl)phosphonium chloride soln. 124 parts, squeezed to 75% wet pickup, and dried at 3 min. at 85 C. to approx. 15% moisture content. The dry fabric was treated 6 min. in a (II) chamber to give fabric which passed the std. vertical flame test with a char length of 4.2 in. and had a warp breaking strength of 143.8 lb. compared to 124.4 lb. for untrd. fabric.

352. Beninate, J. V.; Perkins, R. M.; Drake, G. L., Jr.; Reeves, W. A. Economical durable flame-retardant finish for cotton. Textile Res. J. 39, no. 4:368-74(April, 1969); ABIPC 40:A3730.

A no. of different N-methylol cpds. have been incorporated with tetrakis-(hydroxymethyl)phosphonium hydroxide (THPOH) with the objective of prodg. a more economical durable flame-retardant finish for cotton. The use of trimethylol-melamine (TMM) with THPOH resulted in more efficient trmts. than those in which dimethylolethyleneurea or dimethylolmethoxyethyl carbamate was used. Flame resistance was imparted to cotton fabric by trmt. with THPOH-TMM and chemically curing with ammonia vapor fld. by a heat cure. There was no redn. in tensile strength of fabrics trd. by this process; however, moderate tear strength losses were observed. Higher resin add-on was required to render fabrics flame resistant when THPOH-TMM was appl. by a pad-dry-cure process. Durable flame resistance was imparted to fabrics trd. with solns. contg. THPOH-TMM at molar ratios of 3:1, 2:1, and 1:1. Larger amts. of TMM in the solns. resulted in decreased flame resistance. Solns. contg. 13.4% THPOH and 16.8% TMM were effective in imparting durable flame resistance to fabrics.

353. Bernskiold, A. Phosphorus chemicals as flame retardant agents for cellulose fabrics. Mod. Kemi no. 10:40-2(1970); CA 75:A7169.

354. Bilger, X. F. Novel nitrogen-containing organophosphorus compounds. Brit. pat. 1,036,153(July 13, 1966); ABIPC 38:A1354.

A process for prepg. flameproofing agents for use in trg. cellulosic fibers comprises reacting certain P cpds. first with ammonia and then with MeOH, the P cpds. having the formula $P(sub\ n)N(sub\ n-1)\ Cl(sub\ 2n +3)$, in which n has a value of at least 2. The reaction is carried out in an inert solvent, at a temp. of -10 C. to +50 C.

355. Bilger, X. F.; Mangeney, G. Flameproofing textiles with phosphorous- and nitrogen-containing products. Melliand Textilber. 46, no. 3:294-300(March, 1965); Ger.; ABIPC 36:A94.

Flg. a rev. of the mechanism of thermal degradation and combustion of cellulose and of the theoret. basis of flameproof finishing, the main prods.

(incl. cpds. of phosphoric acid with N-contg. substances, such as urea, dicyandiamide, melamine, guanidine, etc.; aziridine (ethylenimine) derivs.; triallyl-
phosphates and derivs.; phosphonium derivs.; and polymeric phosphonitrile chloride
derivs.; and processes employed in the flameproofing of textiles (particularly
cellulosic textiles) are summarized along with the rel. flameproofing effect
obtained with the various prods. and processes. 85 ref.

356. Bitterli, W. Combustion behavior of textiles from different fibers.
Textilveredlung 6, no. 10:660-4(1971); Ger.; CA 76:A26273.

Polyester, rayon, and polyamide fabrics and double-layer laminates made
from them and cotton or wool fabrics had low burning rates and burning times,
but blends of natural fibers alone, such as cotton-wool blends, burned for much
longer times at high burning. Double layer laminates contg. flameproofed cotton
showed good fire resistance. An app. which recorded the propagation of the
flame made possible the detection and recording of uniform, accelerating, and
decelerating burning rates. Wearing a flame-resistant cellulose fabric hindered
the burning of other synt. matls. worn simult.

357. Blackburn, D.; Haslam, E. Fireproofing of cellulosic material. Brit.
pat. 1,110,116(April 18, 1968); ABIPC 39:A4968.

A process for improving the fire resistance of cellulosic textiles comprises
impregnating the textile with an aq. soln. of a nonvolatile inorg. acid, cyanamide, and a halogenated alkyl phosphate, and heating the impregnated textile.
For example, the trg. soln. can include phosphoric acid, cyanamide, and mixed
chloroethyl phosphates.

358. Blackburn, D.; Haslam, E. Process for improving the fire-resistance
of cellulosic material. Can. pat. 788,894(July 2, 1968); ABIPC 39:A4969.

A process for improving the fire resistance of a cellulosic textile comprises
impregnating the textile with an aq. soln. of a nonvolatile inorg. acid, cyanamide, and a halogenated alkyl phosphate, fld. by heating the impregnated matl.

359. Blackburn, D.; Haslam, E. Treatment of cellulosic textile materials
to provide fire resistance thereto. U.S. pat. 3,567,359(March 2, 1971); ABIPC
42:A2885.

A process for improving the fire-resistance of cellulosic matl. comprises
impregnating the matl. with an aq. soln. of a nonvolatile inorg. acid (e.g.,
phosphoric acid), cyanamide, and a halogenated alkyl phosphate (e.g., mixed
chloroethyl phosphates), and heating to effect reaction between the cellulosic
matl. and the impregnants.

360. Braune, P.; Pohlemann, H.; Swoboda, J.; Wurmb, R. Process for the
manufacture of flame-resistant regenerated cellulose material. Ger. pat. 1,904,427
(Aug. 13, 1970); ABIPC 42:A652.

Phosphonitrile cpds. obtained by reacting a phosphonitrile chloride mixt.
(incl. cyclic oligomers) with n-butylamine and di-n-butylamine in benzene soln.
at 40-70 C. are used as flameproofing additives in the spinning of viscose rayon
fibers. The cpds. impart flame-resistance without adversely affecting the dyeing
or mech. strength props. of the fibers.

361. Brysson, R. J.; Piccolo, B.; Walker, A. M. Calcium-phosphorus deposition during home laundering. Text. Res. J. 41, no. 1:86-7(1971); CA 75:A89453.

362. Bullock, J. B.; Welch, C. M. Process of treating cellulose textiles with polyvinyl chloride polymers, a polysiloxane and zirconium acetate and optionally with flame-resistant and rot-resistant agents. U.S. pat. 3,318,659 (May 9, 1967); ABIPC 38:A2890.

A process for rendering cellulosic textiles water-repellent and weather-resistant comprises wetting the textile with an aq. emulsion contg. 1-20% by wt. of a resin such as PVC, 1-20% of methyl hydrogen polysiloxane, and 0.5-8.0% zirconium acetate, and then dry-curing the textile at 80-180 C. for 1-10 min.

363. Bullock, J. B.; Welch, C. M. Weathering durability of cotton fabrics treated with APO [tris(1-aziridinyl)phosphine]-THPC [tetrakis(hydroxymethyl) phosphonium chloride] flame retardant. Textile Res. J. 36, no. 5:441-51(May, 1966); ABIPC 37:A4099.

The mole ratio of APO/THPC used in the APO-THPC flame-retardant finish for cotton governs to some extent the durability of this finish to outdoor weathering. The durability of this finish was studied by means of natural and artificial weathering tests. APO/THPC mole ratios of 2:1-8:1 were more durable than the std. 1:1 ratio. Photoactive dyes accelerated the outdoor weathering by as much as a factor of 5. The effect of mole ratio on the rate of resin removal was gen. the same in the presence or absence of the dye. Appln. of the dye prior to the resin trmt. caused a more rapid loss of resin than did the reverse order of trmt. Increased APO/THPC mole ratios also increased the strength retention of undyed fabrics during weathering. These same effects occurred in Weather-Ometer tests (simulated weathering tests) made in the absence and presence of photoactive dyes. On undyed fabrics, the percentage loss of breaking strength was often approx. equal to the percentage losses of P and N, esp. when high mole ratios of APO/THPC were used. The Cl content of the resin trd. fabrics suggests at least 2 modes of APO-THPC copolymer formation.

364. Burgazzi, C. Fireproofing of manufactured textiles. Tinctoria 65, no. 12:384-92(1968); 66, no. 1:11-17(1969); Ital.; CA 71:A31218.

This is a review with 36 ref. of various trmts. available for fireproofing natural and synt. fiber textiles with an appendix giving various test procedures. The international requirements for the fireproofing of textiles are discussed together with the mechanism and theory of combustion for cellulose and the fire-proofing trmts. available. The flammability of cotton, viscose, polynosic flock, acetates, wool, silk, polyamide, polyester, and polyacrylonitrile fabrics and mixts. is described. The props. of the fabrics after trmt. are also considered.

365. Burkitt, F. H.; Heap, S. A. Chemical finishing of textiles. Rev. Progr. Coloration 2:51-61(May, 1971); ABIPC 42:A6654.

The chem. finishing of wool fabrics to prevent shrinking and yellowing, and of cellulosic fabrics to impart easy-care finishes, promote flame-, soil-, and weather-resistance, water- and oil-repellency, and rotproofness are revd. 233 ref.

366. Byrne, G. A.; Gardiner, D.; Holmes, F. H. The pyrolysis of cellulose and the action of flame-retardants. (2) Further analysis and identification of products. J. Appl. Chem. 16, no. 3:81-8(March, 1966); ABIPC 37:A1805.

Prods. from the vacuum pyrolysis of cotton cellulose, with or without flame-retardants, at temps. near 420 C. have been identified and detd. In the tar, levoglucosan was detd. by an IR absorption method, and by gas-liquid chromat. of its trimethylsilyl ether; 5-(hydroxymethyl)furfural and 1,6-anhydro-beta-D-glucofuranose were identified and detd. similarly by gas-liquid chromat. Thin-layer chromat. of the 2,4-dinitrophenylhydrazones revealed the identity of 19 carbonyl cpds. in the prods. from pure cotton; fewer were found from cotton trd. with flame-retardants. The distribution of B, N, P, and Cl from appropriate flame-retardants was detd. among the prods. of pyrolysis. It is concluded that borax/boric acid and APO-THPC [a flame retardant based on tris-(1-aziridinyl)-phosphine oxide and tetrakis(hydroxymethyl)phosphonium chloride] act predominantly in the solid phase; Proban (cf. Part 1, Abstr. No. 420) appears to act partly in the vapor phase. Mechanisms of pyrolysis are proposed. In a pure cotton cellulose, 1,2-anhydroglucoses are regarded as important intermediates. 33 ref.

367. Carroll-Porczynski, C. Z. Behavior of nonflammable fibers in mixed textiles. Spinner, Weber, Textilveredl. 89, no. 6:571-4(1971); Ger.; CA 75:A119117.

The flammability and afterglow characs. of blended fabrics contg. non-flammable fibers could not be predicted from the behavior of the individual components. Many of the blended fabrics showed deviations from std. values for flammability because they were transformed to carbon fiber fabrics in which the fiber structure was retained and which had excellent fire resistance. Fibers studied included modacrylics, PVC, Nomex and rayon.

368. Chance, L. H. Process for treating cotton textiles with N,N'-ethylene bis[P,P-bis(aziridinyl)-N-methyl phosphinic amide]. U.S. pat. 3,205,034(Sept. 7, 1965); ABIPC 36:A5731.

The textile is heat-cured after trmt. with the title cpd. to yield a prod. having dimensional stability, crease resistance, and flame resistance. The process can also be appl. to the trmt. of paper.

369. Chance, L. H.; Drake, G. L., Jr.; Reeves, W. A. Flame-inhibiting finishing of cellulose fibers. Melliand Textilber. Int. 52, no. 10:1211-14 (1971); Ger.; CA 76:A26235.

370. Chance, L. H.; Drake, G. L., Jr.; Reeves, W. A. Process for flame-proofing cellulosic material. U.S. pat. 3,403,044(Sept. 24, 1968); ABIPC 39:A6807.

Cellulosic matls., incl. cotton textiles and paper and the like, are rendered flame-retardant by trmt. with aq. precondensates of tetrakis(hydroxymethyl)-phosphonium chloride and phosphoroxytriamide or dimethylamidophosphoroxy diamide, fld. by heating at 80-155 C. for 5 min. to 24 hr. Prior to the heating step, the precondensate can be insolubilized, if desired, by trmt. with ammonia.

371. Chance, L. H.; Drake, G. L., Jr.; Reeves, W. A. Process for flame-proofing cellulosic material. U.S. pat. 3,404,022(Oct. 1, 1968); ABIPC 39:A7819.

Flame-retardant cellulosic textiles are prepd. by trg. the textiles with aq. precondensates of tetrakis(hydroxymethyl)phosphonium chloride and either tris-(carbamoylethyl)phosphine or tris(carbamoylethyl)phosphine oxide, drying, exposing the trd. matl. to gaseous ammonia at a temp. from room temp. up to about 100 C., immersing the matl. in aq. ammonia soln. at room temp. to 60 C., and washing and drying. The process can also be appl. to the trmt. of paper.

372. Chance, L. H.; Drake, G. L., Jr.; Reeves, W. A. Process of treating cellulosic textiles with methylol derivatives of tris(2-carbamoylethyl)phosphine and products thereof. U.S. pat. 3,276,838(Oct. 4, 1966); ABIPC 37:A7571.

HCHO is reacted with tris(2-carbamoylethyl)phosphine in acidic aq. soln. and the methylol deriv. obtained is used to treat cellulosic textiles to impart various improved props. such as dimensional stability, flame resistance, crease resistance, and rot resistance.

373. Chance, L. H.; Leonard, E. K. Acid catalyzed modification of cellulosic materials with methylolated, halo-cyanoacetamides. U.S. pat. 3,350,164(Oct. 31, 1967); ABIPC 38:A8573.

A process is provided for trg. a cellulosic fabric so as to improve various props. such as resistance to flame and creasing. The process involves wetting the fabric with an aq. soln. of the cpn. prepd. by reacting in a basic aq. soln. dibromocyanoacetamide with HCHO in a mole ratio of 1:1 to 1:3 and from 1% to 3% of an acid catalyst, and then curing the fabric at 100-140 C. for 1-10 min.

374. Chance, L. H.; Leonard, E. K.; Drake, G. L., Jr. Methylol derivatives of halo cyanoacetamides and their evaluation on cotton fabrics. Textile Res. J. 37, no. 5:339-43(May, 1967); ABIPC 38:A5112.

Methylol derivs. of dibromocyanoacetamide (I) and dichlorocyanoacetamide were prepared, appl. to cotton fabric by conventional padding techniques, and the phys. props. of the trd. fabrics studied. Both cpds. improve the wrinkle recovery and flame resistance, but reduced fabric strength considerably. The improvement in wrinkle recovery and insoly. of the trd. fabric in cuene indicated that the cellulose was cross-linked. Addnl. studies with (I) showed that this finish is more resistant to acidic than basic hydrolysis, and imparts considerable rot resistance to the fabric. (I) seemed to offer an attractive and simple way of adding Br to cotton because of its water soly. and the fact that it can be appl. to cotton by conventional padding techniques. However, the sensitivity of the finish to rel. low temps. removes it from the realm of a pract. finish for cotton apparel goods.

375. Chance, L. H.; Reeves, W. A.; Drake, G. L., Jr. Phosphorus-containing carboxamides and their evaluation on cotton fabrics. Textile Res. J. 35, no. 4:291-8 (April, 1965); ABIPC 36:A2384.

High wrinkle resistance and moderate flame resistance were simult. imparted to cotton fabric trd. with the methylol derivs. of tris(2-carbamoylethyl)-phosphine and tris(2-carbamoylethyl)phosphine oxide in the presence of Zn nitrate and Mg chloride catalysts. Strength losses were comparable to those of the commonly used methylolamide finishing agents for cotton. Fabrics trd. with

either of the cpds. were damaged in the Cl retention test. Both of the fabric
finishes were more resistant to acidic than to alk. hydrolysis, but the phosphine
oxide finish was more resistant to both acidic and alk. hydrolysis than the
phosphine finish.

376. Chance, L. H.; Reeves, W. A.; Drake, G. L., Jr. Process of treating
cellulosic textiles with N-methylol derivatives of tris(2-carbamoylethyl)phosphine
oxide and products thereof. U.S. pat. 3,268,292(Aug. 23, 1966); ABIPC 37:A5985.

The dimensional stability and resistance to flame, creasing, and rot of
cellulosic textiles is improved by wetting the textile with an aq. soln. contg.
an N-methylol deriv. of tris(2-carbamoylethyl)phosphine oxide (I) prepd. by
reacting (I) with HCHO in aq. alk. soln., together with an acid-type catalyst,
and heat-curing the cellulosic textile.

377. Chemical & Engineering News. Flame retardant gets plant-scale trial.
Chem. Eng. News 46, no. 39:42-3(Sept. 9, 1968); ABIPC 39:A5535.

A process for imparting flame resistance to fabrics, devd. by the U.S.
Dept. of Agriculture, is undergoing plant-scale trials. The process involves
padding the fabric with tetrakis(hydroxymethyl)phosphonium hydroxide (THPOH) and
curing the fabric in the presence of ammonia vapor. The ammonia reacts with
THPOH to form a highly insol. flame-resistant polymer inside the fabric. Strength
loss after the flame-retardancy trmt. amts. to only about 30%. However, the
process does not impart, nor is it compatible with, durable press finishes. The
process is also limited to blends contg. no less than 50% cotton.

378. Ciba Ltd. Phosphorus-containing N,N-dimethylolcarboxylic acid amides.
Brit. pat. 1,192,837(May 20, 1970); ABIPC 41:A5554.

The flameproofing agents for cellulosic textiles described in this invention
are similar to those described previously in Fr. pat. 1,560,824; see Abstr. No.
382.

379. Ciba Ltd. Process for improving fabrics containing cellulosic fibers.
Brit. pat. 1,190,538(May 6, 1970); ABIPC 41:A5555.

In processes for improving the props. of cellulosic fabrics by impregnating
them with various trmt. liquors (e.g., creaseproofing, flameproofing, and the
like liquors), the absorptivity of the fabric for the liquor is improved by adding
a high mol.wt. PEG to the impregnating liquor.

380. Ciba Ltd. Process for rendering cellulosic fibrous materials
flame-resistant. Brit. pat. 1,139,380(Jan. 8, 1969); ABIPC 40:A3206.

This process for rendering cellulosic fibrous matls. flame-resistant is
similar to that described previously in Can. pat. 776,115; see Abstr. No. 414.

381. Ciba SA. Flameproofing process for cellulosic fabrics. Fr. pat.
1,449,799(July 11, 1966); ABIPC 39:A6816.

The flameproofing process claimed is similar to that described in Can. pat.
775,510; see Abstr. No. 413.

382.   Ciba SA.   New N,N-dimethylolcarbamides containing phosphorus, process for their preparation, and process for flameproofing cellulosic fibrous materials. Fr. pat. 1,560,824(Feb. 10, 1969); ABIPC 41:A593.

P-contg. N,N-dimethylol ureas, particularly 3-(dimethylphosphono)propionyl-dimethylolamide, are claimed as flameproofing agents for cellulosic textiles.

383.   Cicione, R. J.; Kenney, V. S.; Jutras, W. J., Jr.; Gagliardi, D. D. Cross-linking reactions in fibers and multifunctional effects.   Am. Dyestuff Reptr. 57, no. 3:66-9(Jan. 29, 1968); ABIPC 39:A105.

Cross-linking reactions in cellulosic fibers are important for prodg. dimensionally stable, wrinkle resistant, and durably pressed fabrics.   When secondary props., such as mildew resistance, stain and soil repellency, flame-proofing, etc., are desired, these are obtained by using a multitude of different chem. finishing agents in the same trg. bath.   Several examples are cited where other functional props. can be incorporated into a single cellulose cross-linking agent.   The advantages of applg. multifunctional props. in a single step to the textile ind. and its importance in future finishing devts. is stressed.

384.   Daigle, D. J.; Chance, L. H.; Drake, G. L., Jr.   Bis(halomethyl)-phosphorylmethyltriphenylphosphonium halides and a stable phosphine methylene. U.S. pat. 3,607,944(Sept. 21, 1971); CA 76:A15739.

385.   Daigle, D. J.; Donaldson, D. J.   A less expensive durable flame retardant.   Textile Chemist Colorist 1, no. 24:534-6(Nov. 19, 1969); ABIPC 41:A5121.

Varying quantities of trimethylolmelamine (TMM) were incorporated with tetrakis(hydroxymethyl)phosphonium hydroxide (THPOH)-Cu nitrate-ammonium hydroxide soln. and applied to cotton fabric.   Although the flame-retardant finish produced by reacting the phosphine-Cu complex with aq. ammonia is durable and effective at add-ons of 13-17%, this study showed that the amt. of P needed in the flame-retardant finish can be reduced by increasing the N content with TMM.   Cotton fabric with good flame retardancy and strength retention was obtained by using conventional pad-cure techniques for applg. the soln.   This has resulted in the use of lesser amts. of THPOH to produce a less expensive, but durable flame-retardant finish for cotton.

386.   Debenedetti, E.   Lasting fireproofing of cellulosic textiles.   Nuova Chim. 46, no. 1:43-8(1970); Ital.; CA 73:A36413.

Various methods devd. for trg. cellulosic fabrics with phosphorus cpns. to give durable flame-retardant props. are discussed.

387.   Dokladal, F.; Javorsky, J.; Pirkl, K.; Dvoracek, K.   Flame-resisting material.   Can. pat. 813,850(May 27, 1969); ABIPC 40:A5989.

A flame-resistant matl. comprises a nonwoven stitch-bonded fabric contg. a major proportion of asbestos fibers, and a coating on the fabric incl. a polymer such as PVC and a filler having heat- and light-reflecting props., such as mica.

388. Domovs, K. B.; Lee, W. K.; Tesoro, G. C. Process for flameproofing and enhancing the dyeability of polymeric materials. Brit. pat. 1,176,495(Jan. 1, 1970); ABIPC 41:A2524.

A process for flameproofing and enhancing the dyeability of cellulosic fabrics involves trg. the fabric with certain water-sol. N-contg. phosphonates, such as polyguanidino phosphonate.

389. Donahue, E. L.; Donahue, M. S. Method of flameproofing a cellulosic textile. U.S. pat. 3,253,881(May 31, 1966); ABIPC 37:A4375.

A cellulosic textile is flameproofed by heating the textile after applg. to it an aq. soln. of the reaction prod. of 2-6 moles of urea and 1 mole of orthophosphoric acid to which has been added 0.5-2.0% of pyridine, based on the total wt. of urea and orthophosphoric acid.

390. Donaldson, D. J.; Daigle, D. J. Phosphorus-nitrogen flame retardant via copper complex. Textile Res. J. 39, no. 4:363-7(April, 1969); ABIPC 40:A3735.

Copper salts were found to stabilize tetrakis(hydroxymethyl)phosphonium hydroxide (THPOH)-ammonium hydroxide solns. by formation of a complex thereby making it possible to apply THPOH to cotton fabric without the use of gaseous ammonia. The soln. was prepd. by adding cupric nitrate and ammonium hydroxide to aq. THPOH. The process consisted of padding the fabrics with the soln. and either curing immediately or placing the fabrics in sealed plastic bags for 18 hr. and then curing for 5-10 min. at 130-160 C. Greater efficiency was obtained by curing immediately after padding. Cotton fabric trd. by this process had good flame retardency and passed the std. vert. flame test after 25 launderings. There was little loss of strength.

391. Dorset, B. C. M. Developments in flameproofing treatments and techniques. Text. Mfr. 96, no. 1146:240-6(1970); Engl.; CA 73:A36330.

392. Dorset, B. C. M. Flame retardant and crease-resist finishing processes. Text. Mfr. 97, no. 1154:68-75(1971); CA 75:A22203.

393. Drake, G. L., Jr. Fire retardancy: its status today. Am. Dyest. Rep. 60, no. 5:43-4, 46-7(1971); Engl.; CA 75:A50280.

A rev. with 27 ref. is presented. Fire retardation in cotton and polyester-cotton blend fabrics is discussed.

394. Drake, G. L., Jr. Flame resistant and rot resistant finishes: application to cellulose. Am. Dyestuff Reptr. 56, no. 15:P560-4(July 17, 1967); ABIPC 38:A6584.

Flame- and rotproofing of cotton are revd. The gen. requirements of a flame retardant are listed and the flameproofing of cotton with inorg. flame-proofing cpds., tetrakis(hydroxymethyl)phosphonium chloride, and tris(1-aziridinyl)phosphine oxide are discussed. Rot and mildewproofing of cotton through chem. modification of the cellulose, by appln. of methylolmelamine resins, acid colloids, Zr-antimicrobial agents, appln. of an antimicrobial agent during finishing, and by mineral dyeing with a Cr-Zr complex are also revd. 24 ref.

395. Drake, G. L., Jr.; Perkins, R. M.; Reeves, W. A. Special finishes for textile-flame retardant finishes and soil resistant finishes. Colourage 18, no. 17:35-44, 56(1971); Engl.; CA 76:A4804.

Fire retardant finishes for cotton and cotton-polyester textiles contg. 65% or more of cotton were prepd. from tetrakis(hydroxymethyl)phosphonium chloride (I) or tetrakis(hydroxymethyl)phosphonium hydroxide which are curable by heat and/or ammonia. CMC was used in the presence of a cross-linking agent as an antisoiling finish for cotton and cotton mixed textiles. Fire-retardant finishes of (I) modified with amines and amides, e.g., triethanolamine, trimethylolmelamine, and urea are discussed. The use of Et perfluorooctanoate-ethylenimine adduct, fluorinated ethoxymethylurea, and (I) with 1,1-dihydroper-fluorooctylamine for soil release is discussed.

396. du Pont de Nemours, E. I., and Co. Treatment of water-swellable cellulosic materials. Brit. pat. 1,243,990(Aug. 25, 1971); CA 76:A4876.

Water-swellable cellulose textiles or textile blends are continuously trd. with various finishing agents, e.g., flame retardants, biocides, UV absorbents, by successively padding with sufficient water to swell the fibers, the finishing agent, and a solvent for the finishing agent. Cotton is padded to 75% pickup with an aq. paste contg. 2-(m-chlorostyryl)naphth[2,1-d]oxazole 10, diethylene glycol diacetate 30, triethylene glycol diacetate 19, gum tragacanth 6, nonionic surfactant 1.2, and water 133 g. and the padded cloth is heated 90 sec. at 190-5 C., scoured, and dried to yield a fluorescent fabric. Cotton or cotton-polyester blends are similarly finished with other fluorescent whiteners, flame retardants, UV absorbers, bacteriostats, fungicides, or water-proofing agents.

397. Edel, G. Behavior of textiles with respect to fire. (1). Study of the specific behavior of various types of articles as a function of the nature of the fibers composing them. Bull. ITF 24, no. 148:355-77(May/June, 1970); Fr.; ABIPC 41:A6136.

The flame-resistance of a wide range of cellulosic (cotton and rayon) and synt.-fiber fabrics was studied using 4 std. methods. The cellulosic and acrylic-fiber fabrics were found to burn completely. Polyamide, polyester, and wool fabrics gave an initial inflammation fld. by self-extinction. In the case of cellulosic fabrics, the rate of flame propagation was related to the fabric basis wt. Quant. comparison of the results obtained with the various methods, however, was difficult. Studies aimed at the devt. of a new flame test procedure, permitting adjustment of sample inclination, are outlined. The method was particularly designed to permit a certain differentiation between the phenomena of inflammation and flame propagation, the results being given in terms of flame propagation as a function of sample inclination.

398. Farbwerke Hoechst AG. Flameproofing process for cellulosic materials. Brit. pat. 1,131,899(Oct. 30, 1968); ABIPC 40:A471.

A process for flameproofing a cellulosic textile comprises impregnating the textile with an aq. soln. contg. trisaziridinyl-phosphine oxide and a prod. of the reaction of 1 mole of an epihalohydrin and 1.5-3.0 moles of tri-hydroxymethyl-phosphine, then trg. the matl. with ammonia.

399. Farrissey, W. J., Jr.; Recchia, F. P.; Sayigh, A. A. R. Process for rendering cellulosic material fire retardant. U.S. pat. 3,501,457(March 17, 1970); ABIPC 41:A1492.

Cellulosic matls. (esp. cotton) are rendered fire retardant by reaction with a halogenated isocyanate such as 4,4,4-trichloro-2-bromobutyl isocyanate.

400. Fluegel, W. Organophosphorus compounds as flameproofing agents for cotton-polyester mixed textiles. Ger. Offen. 2,010,531(Sept. 16, 1971); CA 76:A26374.

401. Gandhi, R. S. Flameproofing of cellulosic materials. I. Colourage 16, no. 4:61-4(1969); Engl.; CA 73:A131851.

The history of flameproofing cellulosic matls., flameproofing by pptn. methods, coating the fabric with resins contg. certain oxides, and methods based on formation of cellulose derivs. are revd. with 36 ref.

402. Gandhi, R. S. Flameproofing of cellulosic materials. II. Phosphorus compounds. Colourage 16, no. 8:53-9(1969); Engl.; CA 72:A33042.

A rev. of 45 ref. of the flameproofing of cellulosic matls. with (HOCH-sub 2)sub 4 PCl and phosphonitrile chloride cpds. Methods based on the fixation of P cpds. to cotton with resinouse binders or in which P is chem. combined with cellulose are discussed.

403. Gandhi, R. S. Flameproofing of cellulosic materials. IV. Mechanism of flameproofing. Colourage 16, no. 12:47-51(1969); Engl.; CA 73:A131852.

The coating, gas, and thermal theories of flameproofing of cellulosic matls., gen. props. of flame retardants, modern chem. theory of flameproofing, and the levoglucosan theory are discussed with 22 ref.

404. Godfrey, L. E. A. Flame-retardant rayon containing halogenated phosphonitrilate polymer. U.S. pat. 3,505,087(April 7, 1970); ABIPC 41:A1506.

RC filaments are rendered flame-retardant by incl. in them a water-insol. liquid halogenated phosphonitrilate polymer, such as the 2-chloroethyl hexaester of trimeric phosphonitrillic chloride.

405. Godfrey, L. E. A. Flame-retardant rayon containing mercapto-phosphonitrilate polymer. U.S. pat. 3,532,526(Oct. 6, 1970); ABIPC 41:A6671.

RC filaments are rendered flame-retardant by incorporation in them a water-sol. liquid mercapto-phosphonitrile polymer such as the hexaethylmercapto deriv. of trimeric phosphonitrilic chloride.

406. Godfrey, L. E. A. Flame-retardant regenerated cellulose. U.S. pat. 3,455,713(July 15, 1969); ABIPC 40:A4061.

Flame-retardant rayon fibers are formed by adding to the viscose a liquid phosphonitrilate polymer.

407. Godfrey, L. E. A. Flame-retardant regenerated cellulose. Can. pat. 839,801(April 21, 1970); ABIPC 41:A4597.

RC filaments are rendered flame retardant by adding to the viscose a liquid phosphonitrilate polymer.

408. Godfrey, L. E. A.; Schappel, J. W. Alkoxyphosphazenes as flame retardants for rayon. I&EC Prod. Res. 9, no. 4:426-36(Dec., 1970); ABIPC 41:A8159.

A new approach to the problem of flameproofing cellulosic textiles has been demonstrated. Rayon fibers with excellent flame retardancy were produced by mixing a liquid flame retardant with the viscose soln. before spinning. The normal propyl ester of a mixt. of polymeric phosphonitrilic chlorides was particularly suitable for this appln. Fibers were spun contg. over 30% by wt. of this additive. The flame retardant, uniformly dispersed throughout the fiber in small pockets, is retained after extensive laundering or dry cleaning. Fabrics woven from fibers contg. 20% by dry wt. of the mixed propoxyphosphazenes passed a severe flame retardancy test. 35 ref.

409. Godsay, M. P. Process for flameproofing fibers. Can. pat. 769,630 (Oct. 17, 1967); ABIPC 38:A8576.

A method of making rayon fibers characd. by flame resistance involves incorporating into the viscose 15-30% tris(2,3-dibromopropyl) phosphate (based on cellulose in the viscose), then spinning the viscose by conventional methods.

410. Greenblatt, J. Treatment of cellulosic fabrics. U.S. pat. 3,391,079 (July 2, 1968); ABIPC 39:A4991.

A cpn. is provided for trg. cellulosic dust cloths or the like to enhance dust pick-up props. and impart flame resistance. The cpn. comprises an aq. emulsion of mineral oil, an ammonia-phosphorus pentoxide complex as flame retardant, and suitable emulsifying agents.

411. Greenfeld, S. H.; Warner, E. R.; Reinhart, H. W. Bibliographies on fabric flammability, Part 5: Testing and test methods. Washington, D.C., Government Printing Office, 1970. 33 p.; CA 75:A65217.

412. Guth, C. Process for flameproofing of cellulose-containing textiles. U.S. pat. 3,421,923(Jan. 14, 1969); ABIPC 39:A9854.

This process for the flameproofing of cellulosic textiles is similar to that described in Fr. pat. 1,449,799; see Abstr. No. 381.

413. Guth, C. Process for flameproofing of cellulose-containing textiles. Can. pat. 775,510(Jan. 9, 1968); ABIPC 39:A1242.

A process for flameproofing a cellulosic textile comprises impregnating the textile with a water-sol. hardenable aminoplast, hardening the aminoplast, impregnating the textile in an aq. bath contg. tetrakis(hydroxymethyl)phosphonium chloride, drying, and trg. with gaseous ammonia.

414. Guth, C.; Nachbur, H.; Maeder, A. Process for rendering cellulosic fibers flame-resistant. Can. pat. 776,115(Jan. 16, 1968); ABIPC 39:A2179.

A process for flameproofing cellulosic textiles involves trg. the textile with an aq. prepn. contg. a P cpd. such as 3-(dimethylphosphorus)-propionic acid methylolamide, then drying and heating above 100 C.

415. Hantge, H. Flameproof finishing of textiles. Textilveredlung 6, no. 10:637-45(1971); Ger.; CA 76:A26242.

Flameproofing methods which produce both nondurable and durable finishes on natural and synt. fiber textiles, and esp. methods based on the use of dialkyl phosphates are revd.

416. Hendrix, J. E.; Anderson, T. K.; Clayton, T. J.; Olson, E. S.; Barker, R. H. Flammability measurements and thermal decomposition of textiles. J. Fire Flammability 1:107-39(April, 1970); CA 73:A36383.

417. Hendrix, J. E.; Bostic, J. E., Jr.; Olson, E. S.; Barker, R. H. Pyrolysis and combustion of cellulose. I. Effects of triphenyl phosphate in the presence of nitrogenous bases. J. Appl. Polymer Sci. 14, no. 7:1701-23(July, 1970); ABIPC 41:A7134.

The flame retardance of cotton fabrics trd. with various N-contg. cpds., P-contg. cpds., or mixts. of the two, was detd. using thermal gravimetric anal. (TGA) and differential thermal anal. (DTA). Each fabric was padded with a soln. contg. the requisite quantity of P and/or N-contg. cpds. necessary to attain a selected add-on. The cpds. included aq. solns. of phosphoric acid, diammonium phosphate, urea, and guanidine carbonate, and acetone solns. of diphenyl hydrogen phosphate, diphenyl aminophosphate, and triphenyl phosphate. Rates of combustion were detd. using a std. test method and a flammability tester. DTA and TGA were carried out on powdered fabric samples. The effectiveness of the cpds. as flame retardants was related to the changes they induced in the pyrolytic degradation of the cellulose. Acidic systems or those capable of forming free acids below 300 C. catalyzed the thermal decpn. of cellulose and reduced the prodn. of flammable gas. Urea and guanidine carbonate changed the nature of the reaction energies in the 300-450 C. region from endothermic to exothermic. Nitrogenous bases enhanced the flame-retardant props. of triphenyl phosphate.

418. Heuer, K. Trends in development of filament and staple viscose rayon. Svensk Papperstid. 70, no. 23:793-8(Dec. 15, 1967); Engl.; ABIPC 38:A9043.

Several specific areas for research are discussed, incl. the devt. of nonflammable rayons, e.g., by incorporation of up to 30% (based on cellulose) of wash-resistant flame retardants of the tris(2,3-dibromopropyl) phosphate type.

419. Hofmann, P.; Raschdorf, F. Contribution to the description of reactions of flameproofing agents with cotton and polyester in the pyrolysis range. Textilveredlung 5, no. 6:486-97(June, 1970); Ger.; ABIPC 41:A6141.

Cotton and polyester fabrics, both with and without flameproofing agents based on P and N cpds., were pyrolyzed in N atm. (300-800 C.) or burned in air or a 40:60 O:N atm. Gas chromat. revealed a high similarity in the gases resulting from pyrolysis and combustion in the case of both flameproofed and untrd. fabrics. This shows the dominating thermolytic character of the reaction for both cotton and polyester fabrics.

420. Holmes, F. H.; Shaw, C. J. G. The pyrolysis of cellulose and the action of flame-retardants. I. Significance and analysis of the tar. J. Appl. Chem. 11, no. 6:210-16(June, 1961); ABIPC 32:A706.

The pyrolysis of different cottons in vacuum and in dry air mainly at 418 C. was studied by fractionation and anal. of the pyrolysis prods. The main prods. from a purified cotton cellulose were a combustible tar and water. In the presence of a flame retardant, pyrolysis yielded less tar and more gas and carbonaceous residue (char). The tar was highly flammable and apparently a major factor in the burning of cotton. It consisted of a mixt. of org. cpds., notably acids, carbonyl cpds., and unsatd. cpds., the major component being levoglucosan. There was a direct correlation between the amt. of tar formed and the flammability of the cotton. Removal of impurities from the cellulose resulted in the formation of more tar on pyrolysis. It is concluded that flameproofing trmts. for cotton should aim at redg. the amt. of tar formation.

421. Hooker Chemical Corp. Flameproofing of cellulosic materials. Brit. pat. 975,462(Nov. 18, 1964); ABIPC 36:A1988.

This is similar to Brit. pat. 975,463 (see Abstr. No. 425), the catalyst being a strong acid salt of Mg, Zn, or a tertiary amine.

422. Hooker Chemical Corp. Improved flameproofing composition and process. Brit. pat. 1,065,547(April 19, 1967); ABIPC 38:A6937.

A process for prepg. a flame-retardant cellulosic textile comprises impregnating the matl. with a polymerizable cpn. consisting of a tetrakis-(alpha-hydroxyorgano)phosphonium halide, a water-sol. cyclic copolymerizable N-contg. cpd. such as trimethylolmelamine, a copolymerizable cpd. which is a carbamic acid deriv. such as urea, and an alk. inorg. stabilizer, heating the impregnated matl. to partially polymerize the impregnating cpn. to the extent that it is insol. in ammonia-contg. solns., and then contacting the matl. with a source of ammonia to complete the cure.

423. Hooker Chemical Corp. Improved flameproofing composition and process. Brit. pat. 1,082,677(Sept. 6, 1967); ABIPC 38:A7747.

Cellulosic textiles are flameproofed by trmt. with an aziridinyl phosphorus cpd. contg. at least two 1-aziridinyl groups and a Cl-contg. resinous matl., such as tris(1-aziridinyl)phosphine oxide and PVC.

424. Hooker Chemical Corp. Improved method of flameproofing. Brit. pat. 1,007,580(Oct. 13, 1965); ABIPC 37:A2888.

Cellulosic textiles are flameproofed by impregnating with an aq. soln. incl. a tetrakis(alpha-hydroxyorgano)phosphonium chloride, a copolymerizable N-contg. cpd. such as trimethylol melamine, an acid polymerization catalyst such as triethanolamine, and urea or thiourea; heating; and contacting the textile with ammonia.

425. Hooker Chemical Corp. Improvements relating to agents and processes for flameproofing cellulosic materials. Brit. pat. 975,463(Nov. 18, 1964); ABIPC 36:A1989.

Cellulosic fabrics are flameproofed by trmt. with a cpn. incl. a tetrakis-(alpha-hydroxyorgano)phosphonium chloride, such as tetrakis(hydroxymethyl)-phosphonium chloride, a sulfite capable of combining with an aldehyde (such as Na or Ca sulfite), a methylol-substituted triazine or dimethylol cyclic alkylene urea, and a catalyst such as ammonium sulfate.

426. Itaya, M. Study on viscose fiber grafted with milk casein. J. Soc. Fiber Sci. Technol. Japan 25, no. 6:286-96(June, 1969); Jap.; ABIPC 42:A184.

Viscose fibers contg. 15-20% (by wt.) of casein were obtained by mixing viscose with the copolymn. prod. of 15% milk casein (in 1% NaOH soln.) and 1-3% epichlorohydrin, fld. by conventional spinning. The resulting fiber props. depended on the amt. of epichlorohydrin and on the ratio of viscose to cross-linked casein. They included, in addn. to the usual characs. of viscose fibers, high affinity for wool dyes, lightfastness, flame resistance, heat-insulating capacity, and resistance to insects and fungi.

427. Janku, M. Theory of flameproofing of cotton textiles. Melliand Textilber. Int. 52, no. 10:1201-10(1971); Ger.; CA 76:A26312.

428. Katsuura, K. Pyrolysis and flameproofing of cotton. Sen-i To Kogyo 4, no. 4:206-11(1971); CA 75:A141796.

429. Kertess, A. F.; Williamson, R. [Progress review on] textile chemicals. Rev. Textile Progr. 14:313-27(1962; publ. 1963); ABIPC 36:A110.

This rev. covers dyeing auxiliaries, surface-active agents, chemicals for dimensional stabilization, water- and oilproofing finishes, and flame-resistant trmts. reported in 1962. 93 ref.

430. Krassig, H. Graft copolymerization onto cellulose fibers: a new process for graft modification. Svensk Papperstid. 74, no. 15:417-28(Aug. 15, 1971); Engl.; ABIPC 42:A6630.

The ''xanthate graft initiation'' process (originally invented by Faessinger & Conte of Scott Paper Co.) is outlined. Its advantages for the synt. of cellulose graft copolymers (notably formation of short numerous side-chains and low homopolymer formation) are described. A detailed discn. is given of the grafting uniformity, effects on fiber (viscose rayon) dimensions and fine structure (orientation), as well as on mech. and water retention characs. Pract. possibilities of the process for modification of paper and nonwoven fabrics are also indicated esp. the prodn. of flame-retardant prods. by graft copolymn. of cellulose with P-contg. monomers; the improvement of dyeability by introdn. of amide or amino groups; the imparting of fungistatic and bacteriostatic props., water and oil repellence, and ion-exchange props.; and the mfr. of hemostatic prods.

431. LeBlanc, R. B. Textile treatment. Can. pat. 775,063(Jan. 2, 1968);
ABIPC 39:A2183.

Cellulosic fabrics (incl. textiles and paper) are flameproofed by curing
after impregnation with an aq. trg. bath contg. tris(1-aziridinyl)phosphine
oxide and a thiourea cpd. such as N',N-dimethylol thiourea.

432. Linden, P.; Sello, S. B.; Skovronek, H. S. Flame resistance of
polyester/cellulosic blends. Textilveredlung 6, no. 10:651-6(1971); Engl.;
CA 76:A26313.

A tetrakis(hydroxymethyl)phosphonium chloride-resin based flame retardant
preferentially adhered to the cotton component of a 50:50 polyester-cotton
blend fabric trd. with an aq. soln. of the retardant and the blend was flame
resistant. The blend was also flame resistant when, preferably, the cellulose
component was selectively trd. with the retardant. The chemical add-on required
to make the blend self-extinguishing was 100% or more of that required for a
cotton fabric. The flame resistance of retardant-trd. Nomex-polyester blends
was reduced by the presence of 20% polyester fiber but the resistance of 20:80
polyester-cotton blend was not reduced from that of the corresponding 50:50
cotton blend.

433. Lindner, K. Process for the preservative finishing of textiles
or other cellulosic materials. Ger. pat. 1,276,593(Exam. copy Sept. 5, 1968);
ABIPC 40:A10269.

A process for the preservative finishing of cellulosic and other textiles
or the like is characd. by trmt. with solns. of hydrazine salts of surface-
active anionic cpds. (fatty acids, alkylsulfonates, alkylarylsulfonates, etc.),
alone or, in the absence of reducible or and/or precipitable additives, in
conjunction with washing, dyeing, or flameproofing trmts.

434. Litchfield, E. L.; Kubala, T. A. Flammability of fabrics and other
materials in oxygen-enriched atmospheres. II. Minimum ignition energies. Fire
Technol. 5, no. 4:341-5(1969); CA 72:A80201.

435. Lokhande, H. T. Phosphorus-nitrogen synergism in flame proofing of
cotton fabrics. Colourage 17, no. 16:25-6(1970); CA 73:A78366.

436. Lynch, C. A. Flame-retardant rayon incorporating bis-diphenyl
phosphate derivative of polyalkylene glycols. U.S. pat. 3,556,825(Jan. 19,
1971); ABIPC 42:A658.

Flame-retardant rayon fibers are formed by adding to the viscose soln. a
bis-diphenyl phosphate deriv. of an alkylene glycol, such as dipropylene glycol
bis(diphenyl phosphate).

437. McClure, R. L. Polyvinyl chloride-antimony oxide flame-retardant
mixtures for cellulosic spinning dopes. U.S. pat. 3,575,898(April 20, 1971);
ABIPC 42:A4037.

Flame-retardant fibers and films are formed from a cellulosic spinning
soln. (e.g., viscose) to which has been added a flame-retarding amt. of a

mixt. of antimony oxide and a vinyl chloride copolymer, such as a copolymer
of vinyl chloride and vinylidene chloride.

438. Machell, G. Method of carbonizing polyacrylonitrile-impregnated
cellulose, cyanoethylated cellulose and acrylonitrile graft copolymerized
cellulose textiles. U.S. pat. 3,395,970(Aug. 6, 1968); ABIPC 39:A5895.

A method is provided for making carbonized cellulosic fabrics having
reduced loss of wt. and flexibility and increased flame resistance. The
cellulosic fabric is trd. with acrylonitrile to produce either PAN-impregnated
fabric, cyanoethylated cellulose, or cellulose graft polymerized with acrylonitrile, the total acrylonitrile pick-up being at least 5%. The trd. fabric
is then carbonized by heating in an inert atm. at 300-3000 C.

439. Magat, E. E.; Tanner, D. Cellulosic textile fibers bearing grafted
N-methylol amide. U.S. pat. 3,423,163(Jan. 21, 1969); ABIPC 39:A9862.

This pat. claims a cellulosic textile fiber bearing polymeric chains
grafted to the cellulose, the chains being derived from an N-methylol amide
of an unsatd. acid, the chains being grafted to the cellulose via C-C bonds
in which one of the C atoms of the bond is a cellulosic C. The amide can be
N-methylol acrylamide. The prod. has improved props. such as crease and flame
resistance.

440. Maier, L. Divinylphosphinic acid derivatives for flameproofing
fibers and fabrics. Ger. Offen. 2,049,290(April 15, 1971); CA 75:A22434.

441. Manomed, R. S. Flame-retardant, regenerated cellulose fibers.
Ger. Offen. 2,061,161(June 16, 1971); CA 75:A89306.

The fire resistance of RC fibers is improved by addn. of less than 30%
brominated alkanes to viscose solns. before spinning in sulfuric acid coagulation
baths. A viscose soln. contg. 7.9% cellulose was trd. with 25% brominated
paraffin oil with 58.2% Br and 5.6% Cl content and spun into a coagulating
bath contg. sulfuric acid, Zn sulfate, and Na sulfate at 45 C. The yarn
contained 13.82% halogen and was self-extinguishing (British Standard 3119).
Other flame retardants included C(sub 6-24) alkanes contg. 15-66% Br.

442. Medico, A. Fireproofing of cellulosic textiles. Afinidad 28, no.
286:393-400(1971); Span.; CA 75:A130672.

443. Michel, C. J.; Kuhlmann, U. Process for flameproofing, waterproofing
and oilproofing textile materials. U.S. pat. 3,441,433(April 29, 1969); ABIPC
40:A2292.

This process for trg. cellulosic textiles is similar to that described in
Brit. pat. 1,081,959; see Abstr. No. 482.

444. Miles, T. D.; Delasanta, A. C. Compositions for flameproofing
inflammable materials, such as cellulosic yarns and fabrics. U.S. pat.
3,592,683(July 13, 1971); CA 75:A99238.

Cotton fabric is immersed in a soln. of a P cpd. and a vinyl monomer and
exposed to ionizing radiation to form a copolymer on the fabric and give improved
flame resistance. Cotton sateen fabric was immersed in aq. soln. contg. triallyl phosphate or dimethyl hydrogen phosphite and N-methylolacrylamide,
acrylamide, acrylonitrile, or acrylic acid and exposed to 2-6 megarads irradn.
dose to give 15% dry solids add-on of N-methylolacrylamide-triallyl phosphate
copolymer, acrylamide-triallyl phosphate copolymer, acrylonitrile-triallyl
phosphate copolymer, acrylic acid-triallyl phosphate copolymer, or dimethyl
hydrogen phosphite-N-methylolacrylamide copolymer. The trd. fabrics had a 0
sec. afterflame and less than 6 in. char length on the Vertical Bunsen Flame
test.

445. Miles, T. D.; Delasanta, A. C. Durable nonreactive flame-retardant
finishes for cotton. Textile Res. J. 38, no. 3:273-9(March, 1968); ABIPC
39:A5544.

Tris(2,3-dibromopropyl)phosphate, combined with small amts. of PVC, PVAc,
or acrylic polymers and appl. to fabrics or garments from org. solvents, imparts
a flame-retardant finish which is durable to 15 accelerated mobile launderings.
The solvents used are either xylene, MEK, or chlorinated solvent such as per-
chloroethylene. The finished fabric has high tear strength.

446. Miles, T. D.; Delasanta, A. C. Laboratory study of flame-retardant
textiles produced by an ionizing radiation cure. Textile Res. J. 39, no. 4:357-
62(April, 1969); ABIPC 40:A3745.

Methods of polymg. triallyl phosphate on a cotton fabric were examd. under
conditions feasible for appln. in a com., radiation textile finishing process.
These conditions were irradiation at low dose levels at room temp. in air. Triallyl phosphate does not polymerize to produce a flame-resistant fabric under
conditions designed to maximize the free-radical concn., such as a high dose
rate to decrease oxygen exposure time and the presence of water to increase the
free-radical concn. It was found that copolymn. of triallyl phosphate with
acrylic acid derivs. (acrylic acid, acrylamide, N-methylol acrylamide, and
acrylonitrile) produced a flame-resistant finish on cotton fabric. Cotton
fabric trd. with triallyl phosphate and N-methylol acrylamide and exposed
to 2 megarads of radiation in air at room temp. produced a flame-resistant fabric
durable to repeated washings.

447. Minnesota Mining & Mfg. Co. Heat-resistant black fibers and fabrics
derived from rayon. Brit. pat. 1,144,592(March 5, 1969); ABIPC 40:A4086.

A method is provided for forming black, flame-resistant, heat-resistant
fiber fabrics (woven or nonwoven) from rayon fiber matl. The starting matl.
is impregnated with an aq. soln. of a metal phosphate such as monomagnesium
phosphate, the impregnated matl. is dried, and the dried matl. is heated in the
presence of O for a short time at a temp. of at least 450 C. The fibrous matl.
so formed can readily be carbonized if desired. The process can be modified
by adding a heating step after the impregnation, the optional heating step
being conducted in the absence of O so as to convert the matl. to a black
phosphorus-contg. cpd.

448.   Moreau, J. P.; Chance, L. H.   Flame-retardant cottons using phosphorus-containing triazines.   Am. Dyestuff Reptr. 59, no. 5:37-8, 64-5; discn.:65(May, 1970); ABIPC 41:A5139.

2-Amino-4,6-bisbiethoxyphosphinyl-1,3,5-triazine (ADPT) and 2,4-diamino-6-diethoxyphosphinyl-1,3,5-triazine (DAPT) were prepd. and evald. as flame retardants for cotton fabrics. ADPT was formulated with HCHO and trimethylol-melamine and appl. to white sateen to give good flame resistance and wrinkle recovery before and after 5 home launderings, but with considerable loss in strength props. DAPT similarly tested gave good flame resistance and abrasion resistance before and after 20 launderings, and strength losses comparable to those of typical resin-trd. cotton fabrics.

449.   Morris, C. E.; Chance, L. H.; Drake, G. L., Jr.; Reeves, W. A. Flame retardant finishing of cotton fabric with a methylol derivative of tris(2-carbamoylethyl)phosphine oxide. Text. Chem. Color 3, no. 6:136-9 (1971); CA 75:A50319.

450.   Nachbur, H.; Kern, J.; Maeder, A. Flameproofing compositions for polyester-cellulose fiber materials. S. African pat. 70 02,025(Nov. 24, 1970); CA 75:A50372.

451.   Nachbur, H.; Kern, J.; Maeder, A. Heterocyclic phosphorus compounds and process for flame- and creaseproofing cellulosic materials. Ger. pat. 1,961,884(July 9, 1970); ABIPC 42:A659.

Heterocyclic P cpds. are claimed for the flame- and creaseproofing of cellulosic textiles. The cpds. are characd. by an 8-membered heterocyclic ring and are obtained by reacting phosphonocarboxylic acid amides [e.g., 3-(dimethylphosphono)-propionamide] with anhydrous HCHO (e.g., paraformaldehyde) in the presence of an acid catalyst (e.g., p-toluenesulfonic acid), at elevated temps. (80-150 C.), and preferably in the presence of an inert org. solvent (absence of water).

452.   Nachbur, H.; Maeder, A. Dialkyl[(1-hydroxy-2,2,2-trichloroethyl-carbanoyl) alkyl]phosphonates for flameproofing textiles. Ger. Offen. 2,104,096(Sept. 2, 1971); CA 76:A26372.

453.   Nagamine, A. Durable flameproofing of cellulosic fabrics with phosphorus compounds. Kobunshi Kako 16, no. 8:397-402(1967); Jap.; CA 68:A115569.

454.   Nagy, G. Process of fireproofing regenerated cellulose filaments prepared by the viscose process. Fr. pat. 1,559,000(Jan. 27, 1969); Transl. in Engl. (6 p.) available from IPC at copying cost; ABIPC 40:A9227; 41:A6675.

The process involves incorporating in the viscose soln. in a finely dispersed state 2 to 40% by wt. of an ester of a P-contg. acid incorporating a tetracoordinated P atom and halogen atoms, e.g., tris(1-chloro-3-bromopropyl)-phosphate.

455. Nitto Boseki Co. Ltd. Strong flame-resistant cellulosic fibers and articles and process for producing the same. Brit. pat. 1,174,866(Dec. 17, 1969); ABIPC 41:A1496.

A process for imparting flame-resistance to cellulosic fibers involves trg. the fibers with an aq. soln. contg. a known flame retardant such as guanidine phosphate or ammonium aluminum sulfate, together with ammonium sulfate, sulfonate, or imidosulfonate, then heating the impregnated fibers at 290-350 C.

456. Normand, F. L.; Donaldson, D. J.; Drake, G. L., Jr. Durable flame retardant finish for cotton using cyanamide-THPC [tetrakis(hydroxymethyl)-phosphonium chloride] resins. Am. Dyestuff Reptr. 59, no. 9:46-8(Sept., 1970); ABIPC 42:A1289.

Cotton fabric was made flame retardant by padding it with cyanamide-THPC resins (2:1 molar ratio) contg. 2.0-2.5% phosphoric acid. The finish is durable to repeated launderings. Trd. fabrics had a good hand and appearance, and losses in breaking and tearing strengths were of the same order of magnitude as for wash-wear fabrics. The trd. fabrics did not discolor after chlorine bleaching, and did not exhibit ion-exchange props.

457. Normand, F. L.; Donaldson, D. J.; Drake, G. L., Jr. Durable flame retardants [for cotton fabrics]. Text. Ind. (Atlanta) 134, no. 6:169-70, 176, 186, 188(1970); CA 73:A46541.

A durable flame-retardant finish for both light- and heavy-wt. cotton fabrics, based on the polymeric reaction prod. of tetrakis(hydroxymethyl)-phosphonium chloride, cyanamide, and phosphoric acid, is described. Little smoke or odor was observed when fabrics were trd. with this finish, and little odor was present during processing of the fabric. The trd. fabrics had good hand and appearance and were not discolored by Cl bleaching, but had reduced breaking and tear strength.

458. O'Brien, S. J. Cyanamide-based durable flame-retardant finish for cotton. Textile Res. J. 38, no. 3:256-66(March, 1968); ABIPC 39:A5546.

Studies showed that a cyanamide/phosphoric acid flame-retardant finish can be appl. to cotton in various ways without seriously affecting the hand of the fabric. However, precautions are necessary to counteract a rapid exothermic reaction which occurs during drying and curing of the trd. fabric. The flame-retardant finish is durable to laundering, the degree of durability dep. on the hardness of the wash water. The finish also imparts wash/wear props., shrinkage control, and rot resistance to cellulosic fabrics. The effect of the flame-proofing trmt. on dyes is also discussed.

459. Perfect, J. R. W.; Cole, R. Flameproofing of fabrics. Brit. pat. 1,126,432(Sept. 5, 1968); ABIPC 39:A8855.

A process for flameproofing fabrics made from a mixt. of cellulosic fibers and flame-resistant modacrylic fibers comprises applg. to either the cellulosic fibers or the mixed fiber fabric a further-polymerizable polymer derived from a methylol phosphorus cpd., having at least one free methylol group attached to

a phosphorus atom, and/or an aziridinyl phosphine oxide or sulfide contg. at
least 2 aziridinyl groups, with an amino cpd. capable of reacting with HCHO,
and then curing the trd. fiber or fabric. The amino cpd. can be urea; the
methylol phosphorus cpd. can be a tetrakishydroxymethyl phosphonium salt.

460. Perkins, R. M.; Drake, G. L., Jr.; Reeves, W. A. Effect of laundering
variables on the flame retardancy of cotton fabrics. J. Am. Oil Chem. Soc. 48,
no. 7:330-3(1971); CA 75:A141850.

461. Perkins, R. M.; Drake, G. L., Jr.; Reeves, W. A. Technique for
imparting durable flame resistance to the surface of low density cotton
textiles. Am. Dyestuff Reptr. 54, no. 15:17-18(July 19, 1965); ABIPC 36:A4680.

Cotton pile and nap fabrics passed a mild test for flame-resistance when
the surface only was trd. with various flameproofing formulations. The flame-
retardants were appl. by a spray technique. Flameproofing formulations tested
included a 30% soln. (solids concn.) of tetrakis(hydroxymethyl)phosphonium
chloride (THPC)-urea precondensate, a 36% soln. of THPC-methylolmelamine urea,
5% and 10% solns. of trisaziridinylphosphine oxide (APO)-THPC, and 7% and 25%
solns. of APO. The spray technique results in reduced chem. costs and the
trd. fabric retains its tensile and tear strength. In addn., the textile surface
fibers are made more resilient.

462. Peters, E. M. Heat-resistant black fibers and fabrics derived from
rayon. U.S. pat. 3,235,323(Feb. 15, 1966); ABIPC 37:A1368.

Rayon fibers are impregnated with a water-sol. salt of a strong acid and
a nitrogenous base which is capable of rendering the fibers nonflammable (e.g.,
ammonium chloride), and the impregnated fibers are then heated in the dry state
for about 5 min. at a temp. of at least about 450 F., the temp. and time being
regulated so as to cause the fibers to pass through a stage of low fiber strength
and then regain a higher strength. The fibrous prod. is black, nonconducting,
inert, heat-resistant, and noncarbonized. The prod. is of use in paper and
fabrics having good thermal and elec. insulating characs.

463. Pfeifer, H. Producing flameproof textiles. Melliand Textilber. 50,
no. 10:1229-35(1969); Ger.; CA 71:A113971.

This is a rev. with 22 ref. Laws concerning flameproof textiles, theories
of the mode of action of flameproofing agents, methods for testing flameproofing, temporary and permanent flameproofing textile finishing processes
using inorg. salts and cpds., such as SbO-PVC mixts., tetrakis(hydroxymethyl)-
phosphonium chloride, tris(1-aziridinyl)phosphine oxide, and tetrakis(hydroxymethyl)phosphonium hydroxide, resp., injection of flame-retardants into spinning
solns. for synt. cellulose fibers, and the prepn. of fibers from flameproof
polymers, such as a polyamide (Nomex), a polybenzimidazole, polyimide, poly-
oxadiazole, polythiadiazole, polyvinyl chloride, and polytetrafluoroethylene,
are discussed.

464. Rangarajan, K. Flame-retardant synthetic textiles. Chem. Age
India 22, no. 3:137-40(1971); CA 75:A50272.

465.   Ranney, M. W.   Flame-retardant textiles.   Park Ridge, N.J., Noyes
Data Corp. [Textile Processing Rev. no. 3] c1970:373 p.; ABIPC 41:A233.

This is a detailed rev. of textile flameproofing technol. as reflected
in U.S. pat. disclosures.   It is divided into 9 chapters according to major
types of flameproofing cpds. applied, viz., ammonium salts and borates; Sb and
Ti oxides; amine-P prods.; aziridines, APO, and APS; methylol-P polymers, THPC;
phosphonitrilic chlorides; triallyl phosphates and phosphonates; silicones,
isocyanates, and misc.; nylon and acrylics.   Author, assignee, and pat. no.
indexes are included.

466.   Reeves, W. A.   Some new techniques in cotton finishing.   Am. Dyestuff
Reptr. 57, no. 4:P107-11(Feb. 12, 1968); ABIPC 39:A2740.

Three innovations for finishing cotton textiles are described.   They include
the Zirchrome Process for prodg. weather-resistant fabrics in one simple pad,
dry, and cure operation; a chem. fixation process using ammonia to insolubilize
tetrakis(hydroxymethyl)phosphonium chloride condensates inside cotton to produce
flame-resistant fabrics; and techniques for prodg. durable-press fabrics with
improved abrasion resistance.   The mechanism for each process is discussed,
and advantages and disadvantages of each are given.   23 ref.

467.   Reeves, W. A.; Drake, G. L., Jr.; Beninate, J. V.   Durable and semi-
durable flame retardants based on methylol phosphorus compounds.   Textilveredlung
5, no. 6:498-505(June, 1970); Engl.; ABIPC 41:A6151.

Cotton fabric flameproofing studies were conducted using varying mixts. of
tetrakis(hydroxymethyl)phosphonium chloride (THPC) and the prod. of neutn. of THPC,
''THPOH,'' in conjunction with urea and trimethylolmelamine, as flameproofing
agents.   Changing the proportions of ''THPOH''/THPC was found to have little effect
on add-on of retardant, char length, and moisture regain of trd. fabrics, but did
have significant effects on most other fabric props., incl. breaking and tearing
strengths, and durability of the finish.   The method of curing (ammonia, heat, and
steam curing were used) significantly influenced wrinkle recovery and stiffness
of the trd. fabrics.

468.   Reeves, W. A.; Perkins, R. M.; Drake, G. L., Jr.   Flame resistant
cellulosic materials.   U.S. pat. 3,276,897(Oct. 4, 1966); ABIPC 37:A7578.

A P cpd. such as tetrakis(hydroxymethyl)phosphonium chloride is reacted with
a water-sol. amide such as ethyl carbamate to yield a further-polymerizable methylol-
phosphorus cpd.   An aq. soln. of this cpd., buffered to a pH of 3.5-6.5 with ammonium
acetate, is appl. to a cellulosic textile, and the textile is then dried, exposed
to gaseous ammonia, and immersed in aq. ammonia soln. to effect flameproofing of
the textile.

469.   Reeves, W. A.; Perkins, R. M.; Piccolo, B.; Drake, G. L., Jr.   Some
chemical and physical factors influencing flame retardancy.   Textile Res. J. 40,
no. 3:223-31(March, 1970); ABIPC 41:A7143.

Data are presented explaining how Br and N aid or detract from the flame resistance of cotton fabrics trd. with P-contg. flame retardants.   Amide and amine N
increase flame resistance, whereas nitrile N detracts.   Essentially all the P in a

flame retardant can be accounted for in the char resulting from the pyrolysis of a
fabric when amide or amine N is present. The percent P in the char is considerably
less when nitrole N is present. The amt. of N accounted for in the char is dep.
upon the type of N and the N/P atomic ratio in the flame retardant. Large proportions of amide or amine N contribute to flame resistance in the gaseous or vapor
phase. Bromine contributes to flame retardancy by acting mainly in the vapor phase,
and its action appears to be indep. of P. 30 ref.

470.   Reeves, W. A.; Robinson, H. M.; Reinhardt, R. M. [Progress review on]
finishing cellulosic [textile] materials. Rev. Textile Progr. 15:396-411(1963;
publ. 1964); ABIPC 36:A1696.

Advances during 1963 in condensation resins, cross-linking agents, and chem.
finishing trmts. for cellulosic textiles (rotproofing, waterproofing, soil- and
oilproofing, flameproofing) and prodn. of stretch fabrics are revd. 144 ref.

471.   Reinhard, H.; Welzel, G. Self-extinguishing bonded non-woven fabrics.
Brit. pat. 1,054,877(Jan. 11, 1967); ABIPC 38:A1378.

This nonwoven fabric contains 20-200% (based on fiber wt.) of a binder consisting of a polymer based on an acrylic ester or butadiene, 15-150% of one or more copolymers based on vinylidene chloride, and 15-150% of Sb trioxide.

472.   Reuter, M.; Beermann, C.; Linke, F. Process for the flame-proofing of
fibrous materials consisting of polyester fibers and cellulose fibers. U.S. pat.
3,600,219(Aug. 17, 1971); ABIPC 42:A7142.

This process for trg. cellulosic textiles is similar to that described previously in Can. pat. 846,755; see flg. abstr.

473.   Reuter, M.; Beermann, C.; Linke, F. Process for the flameproofing of
fibrous materials consisting of polyester fibers and cellulose fibers. Can. pat.
846,755(July 14, 1970); ABIPC 41:A7607.

A fabric made of polyester and cellulose fibers is flameproofed by impregnating
with a soln. of the ammonium salt of bis(hydroxymethyl)-phosphinic acid.

474.   Reuter, M.; Beermann, C.; Linke, F. Process for the wash-resistant
flameproofing of cellulosic fibrous material. Ger. pat. 1,930,308(Dec. 17, 1970);
ABIPC 42:A7143.

A process for the wash-resistant flameproofing of cellulosic (e.g., cotton)
fabrics involves impregnation with aq. solns. of methylol-group-contg. urethano-
alkylphosphonates (preferably with the addn. of aminoplast precondensates, e.g.,
N-methylol urea, and/or aminoplast condensation catalysts such as ammonium chloride)
and then subjecting the matl. to heat trmt. (130-180 C.). An example of such a
phosphonate is the diethyl ester of N-monomethylolurethanoethylphosphonic acid.
Through the use of such a cpd., many of the processing problems encountered in
flameproofing with other organophosphorus cpds. are avoided.

475.   Reuter, M.; Orthner, L.; Linke, F. Process for flameproofing cellulose
fibers. Ger. pat. 1,288,556(Exam. copy Feb. 6, 1969); ABIPC 41:A5565.

A process for flameproofing cellulosic textiles involves impregnation of the fibrous matl. with aq. solns. of the oily and neut. reaction prods. of 1 mole epihalohydrin and ca. 2 moles trihydroxymethylphosphine fld. by an ammonia trmt. Handle of the trd. fabrics is not affected.

476. Sanderson, W. A.; Mueller, W. A.; Swidler, R. Phosphonate finishes for fire-retardant durable-press cotton. Textile Res. J. 40, no. 3:217-22(March, 1970); ABIPC 41:A7148.

Two phosphonate flame-retardant durable-press finishes for 100% cotton fabric are described. A system based on guanidine, dimethyl phosphite, and HCHO, applied by a conventional pad-dry-cure process, gave fabrics with excellent and durable flame retardance coupled with moderate wrinkle recovery and strength losses. A system based on methyl phosphonic acid and cyanamide gave durable flame retardance at low add-ons. The latter showed high tolerance for Ca, and produced fabrics with high wet wrinkle recovery, high strength retention, and high moisture regain. Phosphorus-nitrogen synergism and the role played by Ca in the deactivation of phosphonate finishes are discussed.

477. Schappel, J. W.; Bates, A. I. Viscose solutions for making flame retardant rayon. U.S. pat. 3,266,918(Aug. 16, 1966); ABIPC 37:A5996.

The soln. contains 2-40% (based on cellulose wt.) of tri-(2,3-dibromopropyl) phosphate.

478. Sello, S. B.; Tesoro, G. C.; Wurster, R. Flame-retardant cellulose. Textilveredlung 5, no. 5:391-9(May, 1970); Engl.; ABIPC 41:A5161.

N-(Hydroxymethyl)triazine derivs. contg. phosphonate substituents were prepd. and characd. It was found that the fixation of these cpds. on cotton as flame-retarding agents can be carried out either by curing in the presence of acid catalyst or by steaming in the presence of hydrogen peroxide. The cpds. can be applied in conjunction with trimethylol melamine since the conditions for insolubilization are essentially the same. Yields are high, and the chem. stability of the modified fabrics is excellent. While good flame-retarding effects can be obtained with the new cpds., the synergistic effect of the N in the phosphonate-substituted triazine cpds. is less pronounced than indicated by work on other structures. The combination of hydrolytically stable P-contg. triazines and polymethylol melamine, on the other hand, imparts excellent durable flame-retarding props. to cellulosic fabrics.

479. Senez, C. J. M. Improvements in the flame-proofing treatment of textiles. Brit. pat. 1,036,154(July 13, 1966); ABIPC 38:A1350.

In the flameproofing of cellulosic textiles with derivs. of phosphonitrile chlorides (such as those described in Brit. pat. 1,036,153; see Abstr. No. 354), loss of tear resistance in the trd. fabric is reduced by adding to the flameproofing bath an aq. dispersion of PE.

480. Senez, C. J. M. Process and composition for improving the mechanical properties of flameproofed cellulosic textile materials. U.S. pat. 3,232,944 (June 6, 1967); ABIPC 38:A4603.

This is similar to Brit. pat. 1,036,154; see preceding abstr.

481. Senez, C. J. M. Process for flameproofing and waterproofing textile materials. Brit. pat. 1,061,960(March 15, 1967); ABIPC 38:A3802.

Cellulosic textiles are simult. flameproofed and waterproofed by heat trmt. after impregnation with an aq. bath contg., as flameproofing substances, the reaction prod. of ammonia and methyl alc. with a phosphonitrile chloride, and, as waterproofing substance, octadecyloxymethylpyridinium chloride.

482. Senez, C. J. M. Process for flame-proofing, waterproofing and oil-proofing textile materials. Brit. pat. 1,081,959(Sept. 6, 1967); ABIPC 39:A407.

This process for trg. cellulosic textiles comprises impregnating the textile with an aq. bath contg. an aminated flameproofing substance derived from a phosphonitrile chloride and an aq. emulsion of a polyfluoro aliphatic alcohol polyacrylate, and then heating the textile.

483. Senez, C. J. M. Treatment of textiles. Can. pat. 748,480(Dec. 13, 1966); ABIPC 38:A1351.

This process for flameproofing cellulosic textiles is similar to that described in Brit. pat. 1,036,154; see Abstr. No. 479.

484. Senez, C. J. M.; Mourrut, B. Process for dyeing and flameproofing cellulosic fibers. Fr. pat. 1,572,151(May 19, 1969); ABIPC 41:A8632.

A process for the combined dyeing and flameproofing of cellulosic textiles (e.g., cotton and rayon fabrics) is characd. by impregnation in a bath contg. an amino deriv. of a chloride of phosphonitrile as flameproofing agent, an aq. dispersion of a thermoplastic resin, and an aq. dispersion of a pigment dye, and subjecting the impregnated matl. to a heat trmt.

485. Sippel, A.; Engelbrecht, F. Manufacture of cellulose acetate filaments. Ger. pat. 1,222,203(Feb. 9, 1967); ABIPC 39:A4058.

This pat. concerning the mfr. of flameproofed CA filaments is similar to Fr. pat. 1,407,354; see flg. abstr.

486. Societe Rhodiaceta. Flameproofing of cellulose acetate. Fr. pat. 1,407,354(June 21, 1965); ABIPC 37:A8367.

CA fibers are flameproofed by adding to the spinning bath an ester of a chloroacetic acid sol. in acetone and bis(hydroxymethyl)-1,4-benzenes contg. halogen atoms (Cl or Br) in the ring, in an amt. 5-7%, based on CA. Either mono-, di-, or trichloroacetic acid can be used, and the benzene deriv. can contain 1-4 halogen atoms in the ring.

487. Soskind, A. S.; Shulutko, R. I. Method of imparting flame resistance to cellulosic materials. USSR pat. 179,746(Filed May 8, 1963); Publ. Izobret. no. 6:22(1966); ABIPC 37:A2111.

Cellulosic matls. are made flame resistant through the trmt. with Ti-Sb cpds., the trmt. being fld. by washing with water.

488. Stanchenko, G. I.; Ivanova, V. A.; Livshits, R. M.; Rogovin, Z. A. Method of obtaining non-flammable materials. USSR pat. 249,337(Filed April 11, 1968); Publ. Otkryt. Izobret. no. 25:7(1969); ABIPC 40:A8099.

Nonflammable matls. based on cellulose or its derivs. are obtained by graft copolymn. with vinyl monomers fld. by trmt. with orthophosphoric acid. To impart to such matls. a wool ''feel,'' a mixt. of acrylonitrile and 2-methyl-5-vinylpyridine is used for grafting.

489. Stepniczka, H.; DiPietro, J. Flammability characteristics of cotton and polyester fibers. J. Appl. Polym. Sci. 15, no. 9:2149-71(1971); CA 76:A4781.

490. Stevens, J. P., & Co. Inc. Flame-retardant treatments for cellulose. Brit. pat. 1,222,885(Feb. 17, 1971); ABIPC 42:A6105.

A process for imparting flame-retardant props. to a cellulosic fabric comprises trg. the fabric with one or more org. cpds. which sep. or together contain both P and N until the P and N contents of the fabric have been increased to a specified level. For example, the process may involve insolubilizing onto the fabric an N-(hydroxymethyl)-3-phosphonopropionamide in the presence of an acidic catalyst and then insolubilizing onto the fabric a poly-(hydroxymethyl)-melamine in the presence of hydrogen peroxide.

491. Stevens, J. P., & Co. Inc. Modified halogen-containing cellulose derivatives. Brit. pat. 1,082,880(Sept. 13, 1967); ABIPC 38:A7756.

A process is provided for improving the props. (e.g., flame resistance, water repellency, etc.) of halogen-contg. cellulosic matls. (in the form of textiles or the like) which have been obtained by reacting cellulose with a cpd. derived by reacting HCHO with suitable halo-substituted carboxamides. The process involves trg. the cellulose deriv. with a phosphite, ammonia or certain amines, a dimercaptan, or thiourea. For example, cotton twill is reacted with N-methylol-chloroacetamide and the prod. is trd. with trimethyl phosphite to improve its flame resistance.

492. SVF Fachorgan fur Textilveredlung. Special issue: Flame resistant finishing of textiles. SVF Fachorgan Textilveredlung 19, no. 11:766-810(Nov., 1964); Ger.; ABIPC 35:A6191.

This special issue contains the flg. feature articles: Martin, E. P. The problem of combustibility in modern textiles — 5 ref., p. 766-76; Aenishanslin, R. Problems in testing textiles for combustibility and flame resistance — 2 ref., p. 776-82; Bundesmann, H. Some observations concerning the testing of flame-resistant impregnated textiles — 7 ref., p. 783-91; Reese, H. J. The development and testing of flame-resistant finishings [for textiles] — 5 ref., p. 792-803; and Krcma, L. Permanent combined fire-resistant, water-repellent, and fungicidal finishings from organic solvents for cellulosic textiles, p. 804-9.

493. Tesoro, G. C. Chemical modification of cellulose and products thereof. U.S. pat. 3,388,118(June 11, 1968); ABIPC 39:A4044.

This method for effecting the chem. modification of cellulose is similar to that described in Brit. pat. 1,082,880; see Abstr. No. 491.

494. Tesoro, G. C. Flame retardant fabrics: are researchers on the right track? Textile Chemist Colorist 1, no. 14:307-10(July 2, 1969); ABIPC 41:A5166.

The author reviews the state of the art, current research, and unsolved tech. problems in the field of flame-retardant textiles.

495. Tesoro, G. C. Flame retardants for cotton fabrics. Textilveredlung 2, no. 7:435-40(July, 1967); Engl.; ABIPC 38:A5823.

Derivs. of varying N content were prepd. from a com. halogenated phosphonate prod. and used in a flame-retarding trmt. of cotton fabrics through a pad/dry process. The flame-retarding effectiveness of the cpds. was found to increase with increasing N content. On the basis of the results obtained, the ethylene diamine deriv. was selected as a preferred reagent for further study. The prod. was shown to impart satisfactory flame-retarding props. and to exhibit excellent resistance to removal during laundering and to hydrolytic cleavage during alk. scouring.

496. Tesoro, G. C. Method for improving the flame-retardant properties of a cellulosic material. U.S. pat. 3,556,840(Jan. 19, 1971); ABIPC 42:A661.

Cellulosic textiles are rendered flame-retardant by trmt. with an N-(oxymethyl)-3-(dialkylphosphone)propionamide such as N-(hydroxymethyl)-3-(diethylphosphono)propionamide and an acid catalyst, heating, trg. with a poly(oxymethyl) melamine such as tris(hydroxymethyl)melamine and a peroxide such as hydrogen peroxide, and again heating.

497. Tesoro, G. C. Modified cellulose. Can. pat. 773,989(Dec. 19, 1967); ABIPC 39:A2175.

A process is provided for modifying cellulose, e.g., in the form of a textile, so as to impart specific props. such as crease resistance, flame resistance, water repellency, etc. The process involves introducing a halogen into the cellulose to enhance its reactivity, then reacting the cellulose with a suitable reagent to impart the desired specific prop. The halogen is preferably introduced into the cellulose by reaction of the cellulose with a cpd. prepd. by reacting HCHO with a suitable halo-substituted carboxamide. For example, the cellulose can be reacted with N-methylol-chloroacetamide prepd. by reacting HCHO with chlor-acetamide. The chloro-acetamido methyl cellulose so formed can then be reacted with trialkyl phosphites to obtain cellulose amido-phosphonates having improved flame resistance. In another case, the halogen-contg. cellulose is reacted with ammonia, hydrazine, or a polyamine to improve resilience and crease resistance.

498. Tesoro, G. C. Textile finishes. J. Am. Oil Chemists Soc. 45, no. 5: 351-3(May, 1968); ABIPC 39:A3675.

During the last two decades innovations in the textile ind. have produced fabrics mfd. from new fibers or combinations of fibers and fabrics chem. trd. or finished to acquire specific functional props. Durable finishes for cellulosic and wool fabrics (incl. durable-press props., water repellent, stain release, and flame retardant finishes) are revd. Problems assocd. with the washing (e.g., loss of effectiveness of trmt.) of chemically trd. fabrics are discussed.

499. Tesoro, G. C.; Lee, W.-K.; Domovs, K. B. Process for flameproofing polymeric materials. U.S. pat. 3,516,853(June 23, 1970); ABIPC 41:A3491.

A method for flameproofing cellulosic fabrics comprises trg. the fabric with a soln. of tris(1-aziridinyl)phosphine oxide and a N-contg. phosphonate.

500. Tesoro, G. C.; Meiser, C. H., Jr. Some effects of chemical composition on the flammability behavior of textiles. Textile Res. J. 40, no. 5:430-6(May, 1970); ABIPC 42:A207.

The oxygen index method is shown to be a valuable tool for detg. the flame resistance of textiles as a function of their chem. cpn. The limiting oxygen index is reported for polyester-cotton blends, untrd. and trd. with a flame retardant [either diammonium phosphate or tris(2,3-dibromopropyl)phosphate], and for 100% cotton trd. with diammonium phosphate plus either triazine-HCHO resin or trimethylolamine.

501. Tesoro, G. C.; Rivlin, J. Flammability behavior of experimental blends. Text. Chem. Color. 3, no. 7:156-60(1971); Engl.; CA 75:A110944.

The limiting O index (LOI) values for fabric contg. 2-component blends of cotton, Nomex nylon T-450 (I), Dacron T-54, PVC (Chevyl T), PFR rayon, wool, and Modacrylic Verel A (II) showed that flammability of these blends varies considerably. Blends contg. cotton, Dacron, or wool and increasing (I) content had LOI values below the av., whereas those for (I) blends contg. PFR rayon and (II) were above the av. Blends contg. cotton and wool and increasing PFR rayon content had LOI values above the av. (I)-cotton blend fabrics with satisfactory self-extinguishing props. were obtained by coating the fabric with Pyrovatex CP-Aerotex 23 mixts. with 0.5-1.6% P in the fabric.

502. Tesoro, G. C.; Sello, S. B. Flame-retardant tris(haloalkyl) phosphite-modified cellulose and process therefor. U.S. pat. 3,507,610(April 21, 1970); ABIPC 41:A1502.

Flame-retardant props. are imparted to cellulosic matls. such as textiles and paper by trmt. with a tris(haloalkyl) phosphite, such as tris(2-chloroethyl) phosphite, at elevated temp., desirably 130-170 C., in the presence of a chemically inert liquid medium which swells the cellulose, such as dimethylformamide.

503. Tesoro, G. C.; Sello, S. B.; Willard, J. J. Flame-retardant properties of phosphonate derivatives of cotton cellulose. Textile Res. J. 38, no. 3:245-55 (March, 1968); ABIPC 39:A5554.

The reaction of cotton fabric with N-methylolhaloacetamides yields a useful starting matl. for the prepn. of phosphonate derivs. in which the substituent group [-CH(sub 2)NHCOCH(sub 2)P(O)(OR)(sub 2)], where R = CH(sub 3), C(sub 2)H(sub 5), or C(sub 2)H(sub 4)Cl, is located within the fiber. Flame-retardant props. of the phosphonate derivs. are obtained at a lower P content than in the case of fabric where a polymer prepd. from an organophosphorus monomer of related structure is deposited on the fiber surface. Stiffness and other undesirable side effects gen. assocd. with polymer deposition are minimized by the fiber modification procedure.

504. Tesoro, G. C.; Sello, S. B.; Willard, J. J. Nitrogen-phosphorus synergism in flame-retardant cellulose. Textile Res. J. 39, no. 2:180-90(Feb., 1969); ABIPC 40:A3751.

The synergistic role of N in enhancing the flame-retardant characs. of cotton modified with N-hydroxymethyl-3-(dialkylphosphone) propionamide (NMPA) and tris(hydroxymethyl)melamine (TMM) was confirmed. NMPA was appl. by the pad-cure procedure in the presence of acid catalyst and the effect of N was studied using TMM in a subsequent wet fixation trmt. The role of N was also investigated in expts. in which NMPA and TMM were appl. simult. by a pad-cure procedure. Regardless of the method of appln., the flame-retardant props. of cotton were improved. Results were similar with rayon except that higher N and P contents were required. Cotton fabric trd. with halogen derivs. of NMPA (particularly Br, and to a lesser extent, Cl) fld. by trmt. with TMM by the wet fixation procedure were more flame-retardant than those obtained with nonhalogenated NMPA under similar conditions of appln. For cotton, comparable tensile strengths were obtained with the 2 procedures, while losses in tear strength and abrasion resistance were greater for the single-step trmt. Damage caused by retained Cl was significant only at rel. high P content. Rayon fabric props. gen. paralleled those of cotton, but resistance to flex abrasion was more severely impaired by the single-step procedure.

505. Textile Research Institute. Research [progress at the Textile Research Institute]. Textile Res. Inst. Ann. Rept. 1970:15-30 (Princeton Univ. Press, 1971); ABIPC 42:A208.

Achievements and projects in progress at TRI during 1970 are summarized briefly. They incl. the devt. of a new precise test for evalg. flammability characs. of textiles; studies on flame propagation, burning rate, flame temp., oxygen sensitivity of burning textiles, the Oxygen Index Factor, ignition time of flame-retardant cotton goods, and volatile pyrolysis prods.

506. Textile World. Research smooths d[urable] p[ress] wrinkles and improves flame retardants. Textile World 117, no. 11:114-16, 118(Nov., 1967); ABIPC 38:A6597.

Summaries are given of papers presented at the 16th Chemical Finishing Conference sponsored by the National Cotton Council held in Washington, D.C., 1967, incl.: Drake, G. L., Jr.: Conventional pad-dry-cure processes for durable flame and wrinkle resistance with THPOH [variation of tetrakis(hydroxymethyl)phosphonium chloride]. Tesoro, G. C.: Flame retardant properties of phosphonate derivatives of cotton cellulose. Miles, T. D.: Durable nonreactive flame retardant finishes for cotton. O'Brien, S. J.: A cyanamide-based durable flame retardant finish [for cotton].

507. Turner, J. D. Reaction of a brominated N-methylol allyl carbamate derivative with cellulose. Text. Res. J. 41, no. 8:709(1971); CA 76:A15660.

508. Vaughan, J. E. Finishing cellulosic materials. Rev. Textile Progr. 18:358-73(1966/67; publ. 1971.); ABIPC 42:A4613.

Cross-linking, creaseproofing, and other finishing agents for cellulosic textiles are revd., incl. their effects on fabric structure and fiber chem. cpn., as well as special-function performance, notably durable-press, soilproof, water-resistant, oil-repellant, flame-retardant, and rotproof (fungus-resistant, weather-resistant) characs. 116 ref.

509. Vaughan, J. E. [Progress review on] finishing cellulosic [textile] materials. Rev. Textile Progr. 16:308-25(1964; publ. 1965); ABIPC 37:A117.

Interest in the slack mercerization of cotton to produce stretch yarns and fabrics has stimulated further studies into the effects of swelling and tension on the morphol. of cotton and viscose rayon and the relation of structural changes in the fiber to the phys. props. (esp. setting and wash-wear props.) of fabrics and appl. finishes. Interest in cross-linking reactions centered on the length and location of the bonds produced. Condensation resins and special-purpose finishes are also revd., incl. water-, flame-, rot-, and creaseproofing trmts. 172 ref.

510. Vullo, W. J. Treatment of cotton fabric with methyltrivinylphosphonium iodide and trivinylphosphine oxide. Textile Res. J. 40, no. 2:197-9(Feb., 1970); ABIPC 41:A6163.

Cotton fabrics trd. with methyltrivinylphosphonium iodide or with trivinyl-phosphine oxide and cured in the presence of various catalysts showed improved crease recovery props. Some degree of flame resistance was imparted by the trmts.

511. Wagner, G. M. Flameproof polymer compositions. Can. pat. 809,255 (March 25, 1969); ABIPC 40:A3216.

A cpn. for trg. cellulosic textiles to improve flame resistance comprises an aziridinyl phosphine cpd. such as tris(1-aziridinyl)phosphine oxide, a chlorinated resinous matl. such as PVC, and Sb oxide.

512. Wagner, G. M.; Schad, R. A. Flame-retardant cellulosic material. Brit. pat. 1,128,456(Sept. 25, 1968); ABIPC 39:A8857.

A cellulosic textile is rendered flame retardant by heat-curing the textile after impregnation with a cpn. incl. a water-sol. tetrakis(alpha-hydroxyorgano)-phosphonium halide, a water-sol. cyclic N-contg. cpd., a water-sol. tertiary amine, a carbamic acid deriv., a halogenated paraffin, a polyvinyl halide, and water. For example, the cpn. can include tetrakis(hydroxymethyl)phosphonium chloride, trimethylolmelamine, triethanolamine, urea, PVC, and chlorinated paraffin.

513. Wagner, G. M.; Schad, R. A. Flame-retardant cellulosic material. Can. pat. 802,962(Dec. 31, 1968); ABIPC 40:A2298.

The process for flameproofing cellulosic textiles described in this pat. is similar to that described in Brit. pat. 1,128,456; see preceding abstr.

514. Wagner, G. M.; Schad, R. A. Flame-retardant cellulosic material, composition and method for making same. U.S. pat. 3,428,480(Feb. 18, 1969); ABIPC 40:A476.

Cellulosic textiles are rendered flame retardant by trmt. with a cpn. incl. a tetrakis(alpha-hydroxyorgano)phosphonium halide, a water-sol. tertiary amine, a water-sol. cyclic N-contg. cpd., a carbamic acid deriv., a halogenated paraffin, and a polyvinyl halide cpn. For example, the cpn. might comprise tetrakis(hydroxy-methyl)phosphonium chloride, triethanolamine, trimethylolamine, urea, chlorinated paraffin, and PVC.

515. Ward, T. L.; Benerito, R. R. Process useful to produce a fabric that exhibits improved fire retardant properties utilizing halogenated oxirane and thiirane reactants. U.S. pat. 3,563,689(Feb. 16, 1971); ABIPC 42:A1897.

The flame resistance of diethylaminoethylated cellulose fabric is increased by trg. the fabric with a halogenated oxirane in the presence of thiourea, or with a halogenated thiirane in the presence of an alcohol.

516. Watanabe, H.; Yagami, K.; Tumori, T.; Yashiro, K. Process for the manufacture of flameproof regenerated cellulose fibers. Ger. pat. 1,669,491 (Dec. 10, 1970); ABIPC 42:A6107.

A process for flameproofing viscose rayon fibers involves mixing a triaryl-phosphate in which the 3 aryl groups may be different or the same (e.g., triphenyl-phosphate, cresyldiphenylphosphate, o-chlorophenyldiphenylphosphate) with the viscose prior to spinning.

517. Whitlinger, W. Fabric flammability...a burning question. Dispos. Soft Goods 1, no. 3:16-20(March, 1970); ABIPC 41:A4100.

Tests for measuring the flammability of and legislation regulating the flammability characs. of fabrics are revd.

518. Wu, C. Organophosphorus compositions. Brit. pat. 1,215,106(Dec. 9, 1970); ABIPC 42:A5012.

An organophosphorus cpn. of use in flameproofing cellulosic fabrics is formed by reacting elemental P, an epoxide or episulfide such as propylene oxide, and alc. or mercaptan such as MeOH, and an aldehyde such as HCHO.

519. Yamamura, T.; Kawai, A.; Nagai, S. Fire-retardant regenerated cellulose fibers. Jap. pat. 71 06,104(Feb. 16, 1971); CA 76:A4841.

Fire-retardant RC fibers were prepd. by adding phosphates, such as tricresyl phosphate, and cresyl diphenyl phosphate (I) to the spinning soln. A viscose soln. contg. cellulose 9, alkali 6, and C disulfide 35% was mixed with 2.7% (I) and wet-spun to give fire-retardant cellulose fibers having degree of fire retardation 92%, which was decreased to 91% by laundering, compared with 30% for a control fiber contg. no (I).

520. Yamaguchi, H.; Takada, M. Method for retaining flame and soil resist-ancies to fabrics. U.S. pat. 3,436,250(April 1, 1969); ABIPC 40:A1352.

Flame and soil resistance are imparted to cellulosic and other fabrics by trg. the fabrics with a condensed phosphoric acid having a mean degree of condensation of more than 3 and a basic cpd. such as triethanolamine.

521. Yoshida, T.; Katsuura, K. Phosphorous acid esters of cellulose. Jap. pat. 71 10,551(March 17, 1971); CA 75:A22860.

522. Zharova, T. Y.; Tyuganova, M. A.; Rogovin, Z. A.; Monastyrskii, A. G. Imparting flame resistance to viscose rayon fabrics without reducing their mechanical strength. Tekstil. Prom. 27, no. 6:67-8(June, 1967); Russ.; ABIPC 38:A9053.

When cellulosic fabrics are flameproofed by copolymerization, the loss of tensile strength is usually 25-30%, and the loss of tearing strength can be as high as 60-70%. These losses can be significantly reduced if, instead of the fabric, the fibers (viscose rayon staple) are trd. with the copolymerizing agent, and then processed into yarn and fabric. This method caused no loss of tearing strength. The tensile strength of individual fibers was not reduced, and the redn. of the breaking length (less than 20%) could be attributed to the change in fiber wt. caused by copolymerization.

523.   Zimmerman, R. F.; Hoch, P. E.; Wagner, G. M. Flameproofing of textile materials. U.S. pat. 3,247,015(April 19, 1966); ABIPC 37:A2894.

A method of flameproofing cellulosic textiles comprises heating the textile after trmt. with an aq. polymerizable soln. incl. a phosphonium chloride cpd., such as a soln. contg. 35-70% water, 5-30% tetrakis(hydroxymethyl)phosphonium chloride, 5-15% trimethylolmelamine, 1-10% thiourea, 1-1.4 moles of diethylamine/mole of the phosphonium chloride cpd., and 1-10% ammonium sulfate.

524.   Zimmerman, R. F.; Hoch, P. E.; Wagner, G. M. Flameproofing of textile materials. U.S. pat. 3,247,016(April 19, 1966); ABIPC 37:A2895.

This is similar to U.S. pat. 3,247,015 (see preceding abstr.), the diethylamine (used as aldehyde-combining agent) being replaced by a sulfite such as Na sulfite.

WOOD

525.   Allgemeine Papier-Rundschau. Modern machines for manufacture of technical specialty papers: new production units at the paper mill August Koehler AG. Allg. Papier-Rundschau no. 27:1100, 1102, 1104(July 6, 1971); Ger.; ABIPC 42:A5731.

An illus. description is given of modernizations and expansions in the Papier-fabrik A. Koehler AG. in Oberkirch, Ger., mfrs. of numerous fine-paper specialty grades. White water sludge is efficiently recovered in a 2-line clarifier instal-lation and sold after thickening and drying as bonded pellets (granules) which have been chem. trd. to provide a flameproofing cpn. for the woodworking ind.

526.   Andrews, H. J. Introduction to timber engineering. N.Y., Pergamon Press, c1967:221 p.; ABIPC 38:A7645.

In 11 chapters the author deals with timber compared to other structural matls., current practices in timber eng. (incl. N.Am. & Europ. devts.), strength and phys. props. (fire resistance, moisture content, etc.), structural forms (glued and mech. joints), design (of beams, portal frames, columns, etc.), prodn. stds. and codes, drawings, delivery and erection, and preservation against decay.

527.   Blunt, G. V. D. Fireproofing timber. Brit. pat. 1,171,475(Nov. 19, 1969); ABIPC 41:A3902.

A method of fireproofing wood under nonacid conditions comprises impregnating the wood with an aq. soln. of diammonium phosphate and trg. the impregnated wood with an aq. soln. of a Mg salt such as Mg chloride to form a ppt. of Mg ammonium phosphate.

528.   Bowaters, Irish Board Mills Ltd. Stratified, flame-retardant, agglomer-
ated wood fibers. Fr. Demande 2,034,114(Jan., 1971); CA 75:A50638.

A fire resistant wood composite was prepd. by compressing a layer prepd. from
wet wood fibers and a wet top layer, contg. wood fibers, starch, and asbestos that
had been sprayed with an aq. fire retardant cpn. contg. Polybor, Urea FX, and
Formol, which penetrated to the bottom layer, and drying. When subjected to flames,
the top layer of the stratified composite carbonized, giving heat insulation to
the bottom layer.

529.   Draganov, S. M.   Emulsion for preservation and fireproofing of wood.
U.S. pat. 3,378,381(April 16, 1968); ABIPC 39:A3158.

This oil-in-water emulsion comprises a water phase contg. a chlorinated phenol
and a hydrocarbon wax dissolved in distd. petroleum oil.

530.   Goldstein, I. S.; Dreher, W. A.   Method of imparting fire retardance
to wood and the resulting product.   U.S. pat. 3,159,503(Dec. 1, 1964); ABIPC
35:A6846.

A method is provided for increasing the fire resistance of wood (incl. hardboard, wood-particle board, etc.) without increasing the hygroscopicity or adversely
affecting the dimensional stability. The wood is impregnated with an aq. soln. of
dicyandiamide, phosphoric acid, and HCHO, and the impregnated matl. is heated to
70-100 C. The aq. soln. contains 10-50% by wt. of the chem. agents. The dicyandi-
amide:phosphoric acid molar ratio is 1:1 to 2:1, and the soln. contains 0.05-0.15
mole HCHO per mole dicyandiamide.

531.   Gromovoi, I. V.   Finishing of wood [and wood products] with metal
coatings.   Derevoobrabat. Prom. 18, no. 4:9-10(1969); Russ.; ABIPC 40:A3924.

Coating of wood, fiberboards, and wood-particle boards with metallic films
increases the flame resistance of the prods., their resistance to atm. factors,
and improves their appearance. To obtain strongly adhering uniform films, molten
metal is applied to thoroughly cleaned surfaces roughened by trmt. with compressed
air, abrasives, or any other suitable means. The moisture content of the prods.
to be metallized should not exceed 6-10%. To apply the coating, metal wires are
melted in an elec. arc and the metal is sprayed by means of a jet of compressed air.
The metals used include Al, Cu, steel, brass, etc. Two wires of different metals
can be used to obtain a variety of colors, provided their m.p. do not differ greatly.
The coated surfaces can be subsequently trd. to make them dull, semiglossy, or
glossy. Results of flammability and film adhesion tests on metallized wood and
wood-particle boards are given.

532.   Hooker Chemical Corp.   Fire retardant epoxy resin compositions. Brit.
pat. 1,159,821(July 30, 1969); ABIPC 40:A6978.

A method of applg. a fire-retardant cpn. to a cellulosic matl. (e.g., a wood
prod.) comprises applg. to the substrate a low-viscy. cpn. of an epoxy resin in the
form of an epoxy ether having a mol.wt. of 340-8000 and a 1,2 epoxy equivalency
greater than 1, a curing agent for the resin, and a neut. organophosphorus ester,
allowing the cpn. to penetrate the substrate, and then curing at a temp. of 20-250 C.

533. Hsieh, T.-C. A comparative test on the fire retardance of wood treated with five kinds of chemicals. Tai-wan Lin Yeh Shi Yen So Pao Kao no. 197:16(1970); Chinese; CA 75:A130909.

A 2-factorial (chems. and heating time) exptl. design was to det. the effectiveness of fire-retardant chemicals, namely: (1) mixt. of 10% ammonium sulfate and 10% boric acid, (2) a mixt. of 10% Na phosphate (I) and 10% Na tetraborate decahydrate, (3) a mixt. of 10% Na carbonate (II) and 10% (I), (4) a mixt. of 10% diammonium phosphate and 10% Na tetraborate decahydrate, and (5) a mixt. of 10% Na silicate and 10% (II). The heating periods were 1, 2, and 3 min. The temp. of the alc. burner flame in contact with specimens was 660 plus or minus 2 C. Specimens of Picea morrisonicola (spruce) Hay were prepd. by the JIS A-1322 procedure. Samples were fixed at a 45 degree angle. Specimens from (3) were the most effective and the untrd. samples were poorest in all tests, including wt. loss, burning time, burning area, flame resistance, afterflamming, and afterglowing.

534. Hsieh, T.-C. Fire retardance of plywood treated with various chemicals and their influence on gluing properties. Tai-wan Lin Yeh Shi Yen So Pao Kao no. 188:22(1970); Chinese; CA 73:A132172.

535. Ishida, T.; Hirose, R.; Miyagi, I. Fire-retardant woods. Jap. pat. 71 01,590(Jan. 14, 1971); CA 76:A35415.

Beech specimen, lauan plywood, and a particle board were impregnated with 5-20: 80-95 mixt. of fire retardants and polymerizable monomers fld. by polymn. to give a prod. whose fire resistance was better than the wood prods. impregnated with the fire retardants alone. For example, a beech specimen was impregnated with a mixt. of styrene 25, Me methacrylate 55, ammonium oxide 2, chlorinated paraffin 3, tribromopropane 5, and a phosphate 10 parts and azobisisobutyronitrile and heated at 65 C. for 3 hr. to give a prod. having ignition time (gas burner) 3 min. 50 sec., compared with 2 min. 18 sec. for the control contg. the fire retardants only.

536. Kalnin'sh, A. I.; Ermush, N. A.; Podynya, I. V. Flameproofing of plasticized wood. Mod. Drev., 1967:121-4; Russ.; ABIPC 40:A5885.

537. Kolodziej, J.; Ganszczyk, J.; Kloska, A. Fire proofing and fungicidal agent for wood and wood-base materials. Pol. pat. 60,535(Oct. 15, 1970); CA 75:A7661.

538. Lebedev, V. T.; Suminov, S. I.; Shiryaeva, G. V.; Karpov, V. L. Effect of organophosphorus compound additives on the polymerization of vinyl monomers in wood. Dokl. Akad. Nauk SSSR 197, no. 3:601-3(1971); Russ.; CA 75:A22850.

539. Lepage, E. S. Theories on fire protection of wood. Inst. Pesqui. Tecnol., Sao Paulo, Publ. no. 894:85-99(1970); Port.; CA 76:A26532.

540. Melms, F.; Schwenzon, K. Applications of spent sulfite liquor. Leipzig, Deutscher Verlag fur Grundstoffindustrie, 1967:541 p.; Ger.; ABIPC 38:A5357.

Authors and titles of the 24 chapters, indicative of the book's contents, include: Scheele, W.: Possible uses of SSL in wood preservation, esp. against fire.

541. Nicholson, J.; Poole, D. Stable, wood-treating wax emulsions containing hexavalent chromium. U.S. pat. 3,416,933(Dec. 17, 1968); CA 76:A35393.

542. Nunomura, A.; Ito, H.; Kasai, A.; Komazawa, K. Studies on fire-retardant treatments for wood materials. (1) Thermogravimetric analysis of wood and its kinetics. Hokkaido Forest Prod. Res. Inst. Rept. no. 54:18 p.(March, 1969); Jap.; ABIPC 40:A8001.

Untreated sawdust (60-80 mesh) of 5 wood spp. was pyrolyzed and subjected to thermogravimetric anal. in air, nitrogen, and vacuum to obtain activation energies and other fundamental data useful for flame-retardant trmts. The wood spp. included Jap. basswood (Tilia japonica), Jap. birch (Betula maximowicziana), Jap. oak (Quercus crispula = Q. mongolica var. grosseserrata), ezomatsu spruce (Picea jezoensis), and red lauan (Shorea polysperma). Initial significant wt. losses occurred at 180-190 C. in air and ca. 200 C. in N; a more gradual wt. loss occurred in vacuum at rel. lower temps. Basswood, birch, and oak (but not spruce and lauan) showed a slight const. rate of wt. loss between 260-270 C. in air and 260-290 C. in N and vacuum. The most active pyrolysis occurred at 290-300 C. in air and at 310-340 C. in N and vacuum. Active pyrolysis ceased at 320 C. in air and at 350 C. in N or vacuum. Because of the presence of O, wood pyrolysis was greater in air than in N or vacuum. Under equal atm. conditions, the 5 wood spp. showed few differences in behavior. All went through 3 stages of pyrolysis in air and 4 stages in N or vacuum, as indicated by the resp. activation energies at different temps. 35 ref.

543. Nunomura, A.; Ito, H.; Komazawa, K.; Kasai, A. Effect of fire-retardant paints and chemicals on surface flammability of plywood. J. Hokkaido Forest Prod. Res. Inst. no. 5:16-21(1969); Jap.; ABIPC 40:A7893.

544. Petrov, K. A.; Sopikova, I. I. Method for imparting flame resistance to wood materials, such as milled wood. USSR pat. 175,211(Filed July 31, 1964); Publ. Byul. Izobret. no. 19:66(Oct., 1965); Russ.; ABIPC 36:A9315.

Milled wood is rendered highly resistant to flame by trmt. with alkyl(aryl)-phosphinic acid anhydrides or phosphoric acid ester anhydrides preheated to 70-80 C. The milled wood is immersed into the flameproofing agent for several days at room temp., then the mixt. is heated to 130-160 C. for 20-40 min., filtered, washed with hot DMF, and dried.

545. Raff, R. A. V.; Adams, M. F. Flame-retardant wood by in situ catalyzed thermal polymerization of organophosphorus monomers. Northwest Sci. 42, no. 1: 14-19(1968); ABIPC 39:A2117.

The in situ thermal polymn. of catalyzed bis(2-chloroethyl)vinyl phosphonate gives wood having high flame resistance and at least 70% char on burning in the Fire Tube test (ASTM Designation: E69-50). A char yield of about 55% was obtained using uncatalyzed triallyl phosphate. The com. use of these resins in preference to ammonium phosphate may be feasible, because wood contg. these resins does not change in appearance, and is nonhygroscopic, nonleachable by water, noncorrosive, and easy to paint and glue.

546. Rykov, R. I. Effect of concentration of fireproofing agents on the bond strength of wood. Izv. Vyssh. Ucheb. Zaved., Stroit. Arkhitekt. 14, no. 2:79-81(1971); Russ.; CA 75:A130908.

The fireproofing agents ammonium sulfate (I), dibasic ammonium phosphate (II), Na borate, boric acid, and a mixt. contg. (I) 14, (II) 6, and NaF as preservative 1 part were added to wood adhesives until shearing caused splitting along the adhesive layer. The concns. of fireproofing agent at which joint strength redn., delamination of joint along the adhesive, and absence of adhesive hardening occurred depended on the nature of the fireproofing agent and the adhesive. A PF copolymer adhesive (KB-3) was more susceptible to the fireproofing agent than was a resorcinol-HCHO copolymer adhesive (FP-12). The addn. of NaF in the cpn. increased the detrimental effect of the fireproofing agents; it interfered with the hardening of the KB-3 adhesives at a 0.5% concn. The fireproofing agents also lowered the adhesion of the adhesives to wood.

547. Schneider, A. Dimensional stabilization of wood with polyethylene glycol. (2). Studies on property changes of wood through impregnation with polyethylene glycol and the effectiveness of various impregnation processes. Holz Roh-Werkstoff 28, no. 1:20-34(Jan., 1970); Ger.; ABIPC 41:A3396.

Studies show that PEG trmt. in the dimensional stabilization of wood does not significantly reduce wood bending or compression strength. Flame resistance and elec. conductivity are increased while brightness decreases slightly. While the coeff. of friction with respect to steel is not changed, the coeff. of friction with respect to fiberboard increases appreciably. As a basis for improving impregnation processes, the efficiency of PEG trmt. at atm. pressure, under vacuum, and with vacuum and pressure was studied using water-soaked, a.d., and o.d. pine, beech, and spruce samples. Only water-soaked wood proved suitable for PEG trmt. at atm. pressure. Even then, the technique is still rather time consuming. The use of vacuum led to an extraordinary acceleration of PEG absorption in a.d. and o.d. pine and beechwood samples, but not in the more difficulty trd. sprucewood samples. Vacuum had no effect on PEG absorption in water-soaked samples. Vacuum/pressure trmt. further reduced the impregnation time for all of the samples, incl. the water-soaked ones. The influence of sample thickness was much greater in the 12-24 mm. range than in the 24-48 mm. range. The influence of PEG soln. concn. is also examd. The studies indicate that the vacuum process should be used with easily trd. woods with the vacuum/pressure process being reserved for woods which are difficult to treat. 20 ref.

548. Schwab, E. Flame spreading on the surfaces of wood materials. Mitt. Deut. Ges. Holzforsch. no. 56:18-22(1969); Ger.; ABIPC 42:A435.

A discn. of the spreading of flames over the surface of a wood matl. shows such spreading to occur in the flg. steps: warming of the surface area, thermal decpn. of the matl., diffusion of decpn. gases out of the wood matl., and ignition of the gas mixt. Flameproofing agents, such as diammonium phosphate, are shown to act by increasing the WV and carbon dioxide content of the diffusing gases and redg. their content of flammable gases (CO, methane). Flameproofing can also be aided by incorporating matls., such as an Al foil surface, which hinder the initial heat buildup or by adjusting board surface d. or surface trmts. to reduce gas diffusion out of the matl. Problems assocd. with the testing of flame spreading are also considered.

549. Soerensen, K. O.; Soendergaard, J. Fireproofing wood by impregnation with difficultly flammable polymeric materials. Ger. Offen. 2,063,171(July 1, 1971); CA 75:A153122.

Thin wood flakes, threads, or chips were fireproofed with nonflammable resins by impregnation of heated, dry wood with an aq. phenol or resorcinol (I) soln., optionally contg. fire retardant salt, heating until dry, and then impregnating with an aq. HCHO soln. and heating to remove solvent and polymerize the monomers. Thus, veneer laminas were dried at 160 C. to 4% water content, impregnated with a soln. of (I) 10, borax 4, boric acid 4, and water 82 parts 80 C. or more dried at 160 C. to 4% water content, impregnated with a 4% aq. HCHO soln., dried, and heated at 160 C. to give a HCHO-resorcinol resin in the pores of the wood and heated until reaching a 4% water content.

550. Tang, W. K.; Eickner, H. W. Effect of inorganic salts on pyrolysis of wood, cellulose, and lignin determined by differential thermal analysis. U.S. Forest Serv. Res. Paper FPL 82:30 p.(Jan., 1968); ABIPC 39:A3066.

Pyrolysis and combustion reactions of wood were anald. by differential thermal anal. in both He and O atm. on wood, cellulose, and lignin, untrd. and trd. with 2 and 8% by wt. of Na tetraborate decahydrate, K bicarbonate, NaCl, Al chloride hexahydrate, monoammonium phosphate, and boric acid, and 8% by wt. of disodium phosphate, ammonium sulfate, and ammonium pentaborate octahydrate. Results indicate that the net heat of pyrolysis for untrd. and trd. cellulose is endothermic. The heat of pyrolysis for both wood and lignin is initially endothermic, but later becomes exothermic. The heat of combustion of wood is released by flaming of the volatiles with a max. release at about 310 C. and glowing of the solids, with a second max. at 440 C. Effective flame retardants minimized depolymerization, redg. the formation of levoglucosan, and stimulated dehydration prodg. water and char.

551. Urbanik, E. Flammability of pinewood in dependence on the kind and amount of fire retardant in wood. Pr. Inst. Technol. Drewna 16, no. 3:115-28 (1969); Pol.; CA 73:A46827.

552. Zabrodkin, A. G.; Khitrova, L. I.; Solomatina, N. S. Composition for the protection of wood materials against fire. USSR pat. 270,980; Publ. Otkryt. Izobret. 47, no. 17:72(May 12, 1970); ABIPC 41:A5934.

The cpn. contains vermiculite with particle size 0.25-3 mm. and UF resin and, to impart homogeneity to the cpn., CMC is added in an amt. of 1-7 wt. parts based on vermiculite.

Note: This index includes the effective flameproofing agents and compositions,
        but does not include solvents, weatherproofing agents, fungicides, etc.
        Reviews, tests, and testing equipment are also included. If a specific
        compound is not found under the individual listing, it may be listed
        according to the anion; i.e., ammonium phosphate is listed under phosphates,
        ammonium. The numbers refer to the individual entries in the bibliography
        and not to the page numbers.